EXERCISE AND TEST BOOK TO ACCOMPANY

THE WRITER'S WORKPLACE SIXTH EDITION

AND

THE WRITER'S WORKPLACE WITH READINGS FOURTH EDITION

SANDRA SCARRY
Formerly with the Office of Academic Affairs, *City University of New York*

JOHN SCARRY
Hostos Community College, *City University of New York*

Prepared by
Elisa Costanza Affanato
Formerly with *Camden County College*

HARCOURT COLLEGE PUBLISHERS

Fort Worth   Philadelphia   San Diego   New York   Orlando   Austin   San Antonio
Toronto   Montreal   London   Sydney   Tokyo

Cover Image: Tony Stone/Justus Hardin Photography

ISBN: 0-15-506178-X

Address for Domestic Orders
Harcourt College Publishers, 6277 Sea Harbor Drive, Orlando, FL 32887-6777
800-782-4479

Address for International Orders
International Customer Service
Harcourt, Inc., 6277 Sea Harbor Drive, Orlando, FL 32887-6777
407-345-3800
(fax) 407-345-4060
(e-mail) hbintl@harcourt.com

Address for Editorial Correspondence
Harcourt College Publishers, 301 Commerce Street, Suite 3700, Fort Worth, TX 76102

Web Site Address
http://www.harcourtcollege.com

Printed in the United States of America

1 2 3 4 5 6 7 8 9   023   9 8 7 6 5 4 3 2 1

Harcourt College Publishers

ACKNOWLEDGEMENTS

This book has been written to accompany the main text of *The Writer's Workplace*, and again I am honored to be part of such a fine project. Special gratitude goes to the authors, Sandra Scarry and John Scarry, for once again selecting me to prepare this workbook. I am also grateful to Michell Phifer, developmental editor at Harcourt College Publishers, for her support. And, for my former students I feel warm regards in remembering what I learned from them. Once again, you are my audience.

To the three at home, I shall forever be indebted. First, I thank M., and I acknowledge him for his valuable technical support and assistance with the manuscript. My appreciation also goes to him for encouraging me. To B., always a faithful companion, I am thankful for your comfort. Finally, my inspiration comes from S. His courage, steadfastness, tenderness, and optimism make him the best man I have ever known.

**Harcourt College Publishers**

Where Learning Comes to Life

TECHNOLOGY

Technology is changing the learning experience, by increasing the power of your textbook and other learning materials; by allowing you to access more information, more quickly; and by bringing a wider array of choices in your course and content information sources.

Harcourt College Publishers has developed the most comprehensive Web sites, e-books, and electronic learning materials on the market to help you use technology to achieve your goals.

PARTNERS IN LEARNING

Harcourt partners with other companies to make technology work for you and to supply the learning resources you want and need. More importantly, Harcourt and its partners provide avenues to help you reduce your research time of numerous information sources.

Harcourt College Publishers and its partners offer increased opportunities to enhance your learning resources and address your learning style. With quick access to chapter-specific Web sites and e-books . . . from interactive study materials to quizzing, testing, and career advice . . . Harcourt and its partners bring learning to life.

Harcourt's partnership with Digital:Convergence™ brings :CRQ™ technology and the :CueCat™ reader to you and allows Harcourt to provide you with a complete and dynamic list of resources designed to help you achieve your learning goals. Just swipe the cue to view a list of Harcourt's partners and Harcourt's print and electronic learning solutions.

http://www.harcourtcollege.com/partners/

Exercise and Test Book to accompany

THE WRITER'S WORKPLACE
SIXTH EDITION

AND

THE WRITER'S WORKPLACE
WITH READINGS
FOURTH EDITION

CONTENTS

Tests and Exercises

Answers

FINDING SUBJECTS AND VERBS IN SIMPLE SENTENCES

Diagnostic Test

Find the subject and the verb in each sentence. Choose the letter (A, B, or C) that contains both the correct subject and verb.

1. Some of America's zoos are changing and becoming better homes for animal residents.
   A)   homes, are
   B)   homes, are changing
   C)   zoos, are changing and becoming

2. They are more than exhibits and showcases of rare and beautiful species.
   A)   exhibits, are
   B)   they, are
   C)   showcases, are

3. Lifelike animal habitats can be seen more and more.
   A)   habitats, can be seen
   B)   animal, can be seen
   C)   animal, can be

4. These habitats suit the animal much better by relieving the boredom caused by lack of stimulation.
   A)   habitats, relieving
   B)   habitats, caused
   C)   habitats, suit

5. At the Bronx Zoo in New York, the gorillas must search for their food.
   A)   Bronx Zoo, must
   B)   New York, must
   C)   gorillas, must search

6. At feeding time, in the zoo's Congo Gorilla Forest, a bell rings when food is present.
   A)   food, is
   B)   bell, rings
   C)   feeding time, is

7. The gorillas can find their food in the many holes of the trees.
   A)   gorillas, find
   B)   gorillas, can find
   C)   holes, can

8. What did the gorillas do with their days before the Congo Gorilla Forest?
   A)   days, do
   B)   gorillas, do
   C)   Congo Gorilla Forest, did

9. Have you ever been to a concrete gorilla cage while the animals are pacing back and forth?
   A)   animals, are
   B)   animals, are pacing
   C)   you, been

10. Now, when curious visitors arrive at feeding times, they can enjoy a more natural view of the gorillas in their natural habitat.
    A)   they, can enjoy
    B)   visitors, can enjoy
    C)   gorillas, can enjoy

Exercise A

Determine the subject in each of the following sentences by asking the "who or what" question. Don't forget to identify the verb first.

1. With sprinting speeds of about 65 mph, the cheetah is the fastest animal on land.
   (Who or what is the fastest animal?)
   The subject is_____

2. The cheetah's incredible speed depends on some finely adaptive features.
   (Who or what depends on adaptive features?)
   The subject is_____

3. The cheetah's legs, longer than those of other cats, are its most obvious feature.
   (Who or what is its most obvious feature?)
   The subject is_____

4. Their long shoulder blades work with their legs to achieve single strides of 20 feet or more.
   (Who or what work?)
   The subject is_____

5. Enlarged nostrils and a wide airway deliver lots of air to this fast runner.
   (Who or what deliver lots of air?)
   The subject is_____

6. The cheetah's powerful lungs allow the running animal to breathe deeply.
   (Who or what allow the running animal to breathe?)
   The subject is_____

7. The cheetah's claws are always strong and blunt, unlike those of other cats whose claws retract when not in use.
   (Who or what are strong and blunt?)
   The subject is_____

8. The cheetah's claws help the animal to push off and build speed fast.
   (Who or what help to push off?)
   The subject is_____

9. This feature most resembles Olympic runners' track shoes.
   (Who or what most resembles?)
   The subject is_____

10. The pad at the foot's center catches the ground, much the same as a tire tread.
    (Who or what catches the ground?)
    The subject is_____

Exercise B

Read the sentences and decide which letter (A, B, or C) correctly indicates the subject and verb in each.

1.   The cheetah's hard toe pads help the runner to stop suddenly.
      A)   runner, stop
      B)   toe pads, help
      C)   toe pads, stop

2.   Cheetahs can turn or stop suddenly by widely spreading their toes.
      A)   cheetahs, can spread
      B)   cheetahs, spreading
      C)   cheetahs, can turn or stop

3.   A cheetah can suddenly stop a stride as fast as 20 mph.
      A)   stride, can stop
      B)   cheetah, stop
      C)   cheetah, can stop

4.   Extraordinary speed and sudden turning and stopping ability make the cheetah a great hunter.
      A)   ability, make
      B)   cheetah, make
      C)   speed, turning and stopping ability, make

5.   A herd of gazelles can be most vulnerable to a speeding cheetah.
      A)   herd, can be
      B)   gazelles, can be
      C)   cheetah, can be

6.   The chosen gazelle is struck by the cheetah's forepaw.
      A)   gazelle, is struck
      B)   cheetah, is
      C)   forepaw, is

7.   The prey falls from its feet before the hunter.
      A)   hunter, falls
      B)   feet, falls
      C)   prey, falls

8.   Then, finally, the cheetah clamps its powerful jaws shut over the gazelle's throat.
      A)   jaws, shut
      B)   cheetah, clamps
      C)   throat, clamps

9.   However, as fast as the cheetah runs, larger and stronger animals can be a challenge.
      A)   animals, can be
      B)   cheetah, runs
      C)   animals, challenge

10.   Lions can often steal a cheetah's kill, adding to the cheetah's efforts at satisfying its own hunger.
      A)   lions, can steal
      B)   efforts, satisfying
      C)   cheetahs, kill

11. Lions can also be a considerable threat to cheetah cubs.
    A)   lions, threat
    B)   lions, can be
    C)   cheetah cubs, can be

12. Vulnerable to the larger lions, a diminishing number of cubs survive to grow to maturity.
    A)   cubs, survive
    B)   number, survive
    C)   cubs, grow

13. Conservationists have recently taken note of the cheetahs' decrease in numbers.
    A)   conservations, note
    B)   numbers, decrease
    C)   consevationists, have taken note

14. However, these biologists are optimistic about the growing cheetah population.
    A)   biologists, are growing
    B)   biologists, are
    C)   population, are growing

15. Inhabitance in areas where there are fewer larger animals is the cheetah's best chance.
    A)   inhabitance, is
    B)   chance, is
    C)   areas, are

Exercise C

Read the sentences and decide which letter (A, B, or C) correctly indicates the subject and verb in each.

1. Everyone, including the bus drivers, enjoyed the camp trip.
    A)   bus drivers, enjoyed
    B)   everyone, enjoyed
    C)   class, enjoyed

2. Even the counselors, with so many children to supervise, had a day of fun.
    A)   children, had
    B)   counselors, had
    C)   counselors, supervise

3. The Philadelphia Zoo was filled with countless camp groups that day.
    A)   Philadelphia, was filled
    B)   Philadelphia Zoo, was filled
    C)   groups, filled

4. However, the group from Sunny Haven distinguished themselves well.
    A)   Sunny Haven, distinguished
    B)   group, distinguished
    C)   themselves, distinguished

5. When the campers learned about their upcoming zoo trip, they tie-dyed white t-shirts to wear.
    A)   they, wear
    B)   campers, learned
    C)   they, tie-dyed

6. Each of the four groups chose either red, blue, purple, or green.
    A)   four, chose
    B)   groups, chose
    C)   each, chose

7. The excited campers went to the zoo in Philadelphia, the nation's first.
    A)   zoo, went
    B)   campers, went
    C)   Philadelphia, went

8. The zoo grounds are admired by visitors.
    A)   grounds, are admired
    B)   visitors, are admired
    C)   zoo, admired

9. Large old trees reach high into the sky to offer shade to the animal watchers.
    A)   trees, reach
    B)   trees, offer
    C)   sky, offer

10. Entering through the south gate entrance, the campers first encountered the white tiger cubs.
    A)   campers, entering through
    B)   campers, encountered
    C)   cubs, encountered

11. Many of the children favored the carnivores and ran right to the snow leopards.
    A)   children, favored
    B)   children, ran
    C)   many, favored, ran

12. Then on they walked to the African Plains and marveled over zebras, giraffes, antelopes, and wart hogs.
    A)   they, walked
    B)   they, walked, marveled
    C)   they, walked on

13. The inhabitants of Bear Country captured the excitement of the youngest children.
   A) inhabitants, captured
   B) Bear Country, captured
   C) Country, captured

14. By lunchtime, had the campers yet seen the monkeys?
   A) All, thank
   B) monkeys, seen
   C) campers, had seen

15. They all decided to stop for their picnic lunch and save marveling over the monkeys for later.
   A) they, decided to stop, save
   B) monkeys, save
   C) they, stop, save

Exercise D

In the following passage, underline the subject of each sentence once and underline the verb twice.

The most common type of giraffe is the reticulated giraffe. Its colors have a clear pattern of white lines surrounding the darker brown spots. With their speed, adult animals are relatively safe from predators. Additionally, the giraffe's large hooves also help in its defense. A kick from an adult giraffe can be deadly for predators as fierce as lions. However, while the giraffe drinks, the animal must lower its head down to the water. This makes the giraffe spread its long legs to lower itself. In this position, the giraffe is vulnerable to attack because it takes a long time to stand upright again.

Exercise E

In the following passage, underline the subject of each sentence once and underline the verb twice.

Elephants are the only non-extinct members of the order *Proboscidea*, in the family *Elephantidae*. Within this family there are two species: the African elephant and the Asian elephant.

African elephants and Asian elephants differ in various ways. The most striking and well-recognized difference is in the ears of the large animals. The Africans' ears are much larger and appear to be shaped much like the continent of Africa. On the other hand, the Asians' ears are

6

smaller. Most often, only male Asian elephants have large tusks. Conversely, both male and female African elephants have large external tusks. African elephants are typically larger, with concave backs and less hairy bodies than their Asian cousins. Most often smaller, the Asian elephants can also be recognized by the bulges on their foreheads and several patches of depigmentation on their bodies.

Exercise F

In the following paragraphs, underline the subject of each sentence once and underline the verb twice.

Aside from their beauty, the zebra's stripes have important functions. Originally, it was believed that the stripes helped the zebras to stay hidden in the shadows behind trees and bushes. Their alternating black and white patterns would resemble the filtered light of the sun shining down through branches. Actually, zebras are often seen in open areas. This fact, then, would seem to dispute this camouflage theory.

Others believe the stripes act as a distraction to predators who become confused as the sight of a zebra herd. Focusing on a single animal, a lion sees a blur of black and white as the herd scrambles. Still other theories support the fact that the stripes, as distinctive as fingerprints, serve as aids in recognition. After zebras, often living in mixed herds of antelope and gnus, flee from predators, their stripes can help them find each other again.

Mastery Test

Find the subject and the verb in each sentence. Choose the letter (A, B, or C) that contains both the correct subject and verb.

1.   Species conservation is a crucial component in recent efforts at maintaining zoo animal population.
      A)   efforts, maintaining
      B)   species conservation, is
      C)   species conservation, is crucial

2.   Programs of exchanging animals among different zoos for mating have become popular.
      A)   animals, have become
      B)   programs, have become
      C)   zoos, have become

3.   These programs help to alleviate the problems of inbreeding.
      A)   programs, help to alleviate
      B)   problems, alleviate
      C)   inbreeding, alleviate

4.   Related animals, often residents of the same zoo, carry similar genes.
      A)   residents, carry
      B)   genes, carry
      C)   animals, carry

5.   If related animals mate, similar genes combine.
      A)   genes, combine
      B)   animals, mate
      C)   related animals, mate

6.   Inbred offspring are more vulnerable to deformation and disease.
      A)   deformation and disease, are
      B)   offspring, are
      C)   offspring, are more vulnerable

7.   Animals from different zoos can be paired with the exchange program.
      A)   zoos, can be
      B)   different zoos, can be
      C)   animals, can be paired

8.   Genetic diversity, which is naturally present in the wild, can be achieved by the program.
      A)   program, can be achieved
      B)   wild, can be achieved
      C)   genetic diversity, can be achieved

9.   Healthier animal offspring are born.
      A)   animal, are born
      B)   animal offspring, are born
      C)   offspring, are born

Harcourt, Inc.

10.   Through these efforts, genetic diversity in the zoo habitat can be preserved.
       A)   genetic diversity, can be preserved
       B)   efforts, can be preserved
       C)   habitat, can be preserved

MAKING SUBJECTS AND VERBS AGREE

Diagnostic Test

Each sentence contains a blank. Choose the form of the verb (A or B) that correctly completes the sentence.

1.   Vital to the body as the brain and lungs, the heart _____ to pump the blood around the body.
       A)   beats
       B)   beat

2.   This circulation of blood, performed by one of the body's involuntary muscles, _____ essential to healthy function.
       A)   is
       B)   are

3.   Pericardial fluid _____ the space around the heart called the pericardium, which lubricates the heart muscle.
       A)   fills
       B)   fill

4.   The heart, like all muscles, _____ constant blood supply.
       A)   requires
       B)   require

5.   Blood supplied with oxygen and nutrients _____ is taken to the heart by the coronary arteries.
       A)   are
       B)   is

6.   Capillaries within the heart _____ blood to every part of the large muscle.
       A)   carries
       B)   carry

7.   Waste products carried away by the blood _____ transported from the heart through coronary viens.
       A)   is
       B)   are

8.   The cells within every part of the human body _____ oxygen and nutrients to survive.
       A)   needs
       B)   need

9.   Immunity against disease-causing germs _____ also required by the cells.
       A)   are

B) is

10. The heart, together with blood vessels and the blood, _____ to sustain healthy cell function.
    A) works
    B) work

Exercise A

Each sentence contains a blank. Choose the form of the verb (A or B) that correctly completes the sentence.

1. About the size of a fist, the heart _____ as a pump supplying all the body's systems with blood.
   A) acts
   B) act

2. The heart _____ actually two separate pumps.
   A) are
   B) is

3. The lungs and the rest of the body _____ supplied blood by the right and left sides respectively.
   A) is
   B) are

4. The septum is a strong wall that _____ the two sides of the heart.
   A) separate
   B) separates

5. Separation of the two sides _____ necessary to prevent passage of the blood from side to side.
   A) are
   B) is

6. Each of the two sides _____ two chambers.
   A) have
   B) has

7. The upper chambers, called the atria, _____ above the lower chambers, called the ventricles.
   A) lie
   B) lies

8. From atrium to ventricle, blood flow through the heart _____ a one-way process.
   A) is
   B) are

9. Valves, which are flaps of tissue, _____ the direction of the flow.
   A) control
   B) controls

10. Flaps of the valve _____ flattened against the vein wall toward the direction of the flow.
    A) is
    B) are

Harcourt, Inc.

11. If blood does flow backward, the flaps _____ back in place to cause a block.
   A)   shuts
   B)   shut

12. The action of these flaps _____ much like the opening and closing of doors.
   A)   are
   B)   is

13. Channels for blood flow _____ opened when the valves relax.
   A)   are
   B)   is

14. However, with the contraction of valves, channels are closed and the flow of blood _____ blocked.
   A)   is
   B)   are

15. The flaps of the valve _____ held in place by strong tendons.
   A)   is
   B)   are

Exercise B

Each sentence contains a blank. Choose the form of the verb (A or B) that correctly completes the sentence.

1. Besides being a tough sport, ice hockey often _____ to be a beautiful display of form, grace, and speed.
   A)   appear
   B)   appears

2. Enthusiastic fans, many of whom wear their favorite team's jersey _____ a hockey score is the hardest score to make in all of sports.
   A)   believe
   B)   believes

3. All of the game's back and forth non-stop action on the ice _____ aimed at scoring, the sport's main objective.
   A)   is
   B)   are

4. The offensemen _____ toward the frustrating task of getting the frozen rubber puck into the net.
   A)   work
   B)   works

5. Keeping that puck out of the net _____ forth an equal challenge for the defensemen.
   A)   set
   B)   sets

6.   All the while, the referee, wearing vertical black and white stripes, _____ signals and blows his whistle at illegal plays.
        A)   makes
        B)   make

7.   The ever-flowing game _____ at nothing short of penalties and injuries.
        A)   stop
        B)   stops

8.   _____ player substitutions halt the game within periods?
        A)   Does
        B)   Do

9.   Not even the exchange of players _____ the action.
        A)   stop
        B)   stops

10.   The tired players _____ the bench and rested players jump off the bench in their place.
        A)   reaches
        B)   reach

11.   Now the opposition _____ the advantage to score during the exchange.
        A)   takes
        B)   take

12.   Hockey's end then, getting the puck in the net, _____ the players raging on until the end of the period.
        A)   keeps
        B)   keep

13.   The means to the end – scoring the goal -- _____ achieved not always short of violence.
        A)   is
        B)   are

14.   Fierce opposing defensemen _____ every effort of the offence.
        A)   fight
        B)   fights

15.   Then, finally, grueling action on the ice pays off when one of the greatest of all announcers _____, "He shoots! He scores!"
        A)   shout
        B)   shouts

Exercise C

Choose the sentence that contains subject-verb agreement.

1.   A) Many means works to succeed in scoring the hockey goal.
        —B) Many means work to succeed in scoring the hockey goal.

2.   — A) Even slamming one's shoulder or hip into an opponent is legal.
        B) Even slamming one's shoulder or hip into an opponent are legal.

12   Harcourt, Inc.

3.   A) The body check send the opponent slamming into the boards.
   — B) The body check sends the opponent slamming into the boards

4.   — A) Is taking the puck from an opposing player legal?
   B) Are taking the puck from an opposing player legal?

5.   — A) Various methods of stealing the puck are legal.
   B) Various methods of stealing the puck is legal.

6.   A) Filmed coverage proves just how tough many players of ice hockey is.
   — B) Filmed coverage proves just how tough many players of ice hockey are.

7.   — A) A skillful player simply sweeps the puck from his opponent.
   B) A skillful player simply sweep the puck from his opponent.

8.   A) Another crash into him and slap the puck to a teammate.
   — B) Another crashes into him and slaps the puck to a teammate.

9.   A) Once in possession of the puck, an aggressive player take a slap shot.
   — B) Once in possession of the puck, an aggressive player takes a slap shot.

10.   — A) Echoes of the loud boom resound off the boards.
   B) Echoes of the loud boom resounds off the boards.

11.   A) Waiting defensemen spares neither heads nor faces in blocking the shot.
   — B) Waiting defensemen spare neither heads nor faces in blocking the shot.

12.   — A) Once at the net, a player can use almost any method to score.
   B) Once at the net, a player can uses almost any method to score.

13.   — A) An unfortunate goaltender fails in his desperate sprawl at stopping the puck.
   B) An unfortunate goaltender fail in his desperate sprawl at stopping the puck.

14.   — A) Contact between puck and net is made.
   B) Contact between puck and net are made.

15.   A) Goal scoring contribute more than any other play toward what hockey fans call the game's
   "greatest moments."
   — B) Goal scoring contributes more than any other play toward what hockey fans call the game's
   "greatest moments."

Exercise D

Rewrite the passage, making subjects and verbs agree.

      In the safety of the school nurse's office are the familiarity of bandages, sterile cotton, and

antiseptic. Mrs. Gaines touch his shoulder, telling him with the reassurance of the pressure:

everything are going to be all right. In that fact, he surrender and let her clean his scraped and bloody forearm. It really sting, he thinks to himself, but not with the same burning of physical pain. In the moment before he fall, the ball soaring over his head, he know. The bigger boys, in all the excitement of their game, sees him as merely Tom's little brother. Everyone know he won't catch passes like that. What they don't knows is how like salt their laughter add to the sting of the wound.

Exercise E

Rewrite the paragraphs, making subjects and verbs agree.

From his window, he see that snow has fallen, just as the radio voice had promised. Everywhere -- rooftops, fields, bare tree branches -- snow glisten in the clear sunlight. Then, as it will on every snow-filled weekday morning of his hope-filled boyhood, his heart leap. What lie on the other side of the window is hours without the geometry of triangles in math class. There are just white without bells to ring in the next 42-minute class period.

"There are nothing to make a fuss over," Dad call from the kitchen. But Dad don't know this feeling – or at least don't remember. In the days before worry over lost wages or having enough seasoned wood, there are every reason for wonder over this otherwise ordinary Thursday. For a boy of six, something feel extraordinary about letting himself fall backward into the accumulated inches, waving his arms and legs to leave an angelic mark in the fresh snow.

Exercise F

Rewrite the paragraphs, making subjects and verbs agree.

Crossing the back lot, walking through the tangle of dead leaves and brush, I sees what make most people reflects on warm summer afternoons. In the cold air, Mr. Kane's white shirts flips on the

Harcourt, Inc.

line tied from pole to pole. All the trees, except for the holly, is bare, so the flapping shirts makes

quite a racket in the wind.

Something about the scene -- with the crisp sound of the cotton -- warm me inside, just thinking

of all of Mrs. Kane's efforts at scrubbing collars and cuffs, Most of the residents along the lake

heads for warmer places for these colder months. Yet, somehow seeing all those shirts make it feel

like the grand circus of an August afternoon.

Mastery Test

Each sentence contains a blank. Choose the form of the verb (A or B) that correctly completes the
sentence.

1.   The manufacture of all varieties of cheese _____ six major steps.
        A)   involves
        B)   involve

2.   A team of cheesemakers _____ each step in the process.
        A)   supervises
        B)   supervise

3.   A lactic acid starter called rennet and coloring matter _____ mixed with milk in large vats.
        A)   is
        B)   are

4.   After being stirred, the cheese _____.
        A)   curdles
        B)   curdle

5.   Workers in each small cheese factory _____ the cheese into cubes with wire knives.
        A)   cuts
        B)   cut

6.   The operation called *ditching* _____ the curds from the whey.
        A)   removes
        B)   remove

7.   Then the ditched curd _____ piled into large slabs.
        A)   is
        B)   are

8.   Everyone involved in cheesemaking _____ that a good cheese must then ripen.
        A)   knows
        B)   know

9.   Flavor and texture _____ largely upon the kinds of bacteria at work during the ripening process.
        A)   depends
        B)   depend

10.   Nothing _____ our taste more than a well-produced cheese.
        A)   delights
        B)   delight

CORRECTING THE FRAGMENT IN SIMPLE SENTENCES

Diagnostic Test

Identify what part of the sentence is missing and needs to be added to make the fragment into a sentence.

        A.   Add a subject
        B.   Add a verb
        C.   Add a subject and a verb
        D.   The subject and verb are present, but it doesn't express a complete thought.

_B_ 1.   many Americans' favorite game of baseball

_C_ 2.   once the excitement of football fades and winter months move closer to spring

_A_ 3.   is a game played with a bat, a ball, and a glove

_D_ 4.   however, baseball is, above all other sports,

_D_ 5.   the game is played by

_B/C_ 6.   two teams, each with nine players

_A_ 7.   alternate batting and playing the field

_D_ 8.   the field's main divisions are

_B/C_ 9.   the infield

_C_ 10.   covered with dirt

16   Harcourt, Inc.

Exercise A

Each of the following groups of words is a fragment. Identify what part of the sentence is missing and needs to be added to make the fragment into a sentence.

     A.   Add a subject
     B.   Add a verb
     C.   Add a subject and a verb
     D.   The subject and verb are present, but it doesn't express a complete thought.

B 1.   the geometric perfection of the infield

A 2.   can be admired from a fortunate fan's seat location

A 3.   is a perfect square area measuring 90 feet by 90 feet

D 4.   at each corner of the area is

C 5.   exactly 90 feet from each other

B/C 6.   15 inches square

B/C 7.   a rubber five-sided mat which is anchored into the ground

A 8.   serve to mark boundaries on either side of home plate

A 9.   stands inside the batter's box on either the left or right side

D 10.   the catcher's box is marked off

B 11.   just as the batter must stand in the batter's box, the catcher

C 12.   as he awaits the pitch

C 13.   as the batter steps to the plate

A 14.   takes the bat, which is only 2 _ inches at the widest part

A 15.   say hitting a pitched baseball is one of the toughest feats in sports

Exercise B

Each of the following groups of words is a fragment. Identify what part of the sentence is missing and needs to be added to make the fragment into a sentence.

     A.   Add a subject
     B.   Add a verb
     C.   Add a subject and a verb
     D.   The subject and verb are present, but it doesn't express a complete thought.

A 1. became known as the great "Babe" or Babe Ruth

B 2. in the beginning he

D 3. but soon it was his hitting

C 4. a rare accomplishment before Babe Ruth came to baseball

B/C 5. his famous skill

C 6. turning him into a baseball legend

A 7. had his quite humble beginning in Baltimore

C 8. born on February 6, 1895

D 9. he lived over

D 10. young Ruth soon became

B 11. his cursing, tobacco chewing, and running wild

A 12. **placed him in St. Mary's Industrial school in Baltimore**

A 13. **accepted boys who were homeless, runaways, unwanted, or delinquents**

D 14. **at St. Mary's, Ruth received**

C 15. **his first contract signing with Jack Dunn of the Orioles in 1914**

Exercise C

Each of the following groups of words is a fragment. Identify what part of the sentence is missing and needs to be added to make the fragment into a sentence.

    A. Add a subject
    B. Add a verb
    C. Add a subject and a verb
    D. The subject and verb are present, but it doesn't express a complete thought.

D 1. Hank Aaron's birth date was

D 2. like Babe Ruth, Aaron was born

D 3. in 1934 hospitals did not admit

A 4. was a poor family, much like the Ruth family

B 5. being a black American, Aaron's love of baseball

Harcourt, Inc.

B 6. like Babe Ruth, from early on, Aaron

D 7. with nothing else they could do, black players formed

A 8. tried out for the Mobile Bears and played shortstop

D 9. with the Mobile Bears, his first pay for baseball was

D 10. at 16, on a Negro baseball team, Aaron was

A 11. signed Jackie Robinson in 1947

C 12. the first black player to join the majors

A 13. boarded a train, for the first time, for Winston-Salem to play for the Indianapolis Clowns

B/C 14. that traveled the country playing the best local black teams

D 15. playing with the Clowns, Aaron proved

Exercise D

Rewrite the following paragraph, correcting all fragment errors.

In America's temperate zones, autumn's cooler nights and shortened hours of daylight, bringing the finale to the long warm days of summer. Because weather varying this time of year, only the most favorable conditions contribute to the most intensely colored foliage displays. Ideally, nights are cool, but not reaching down into freezing temperatures. Which only causes leaves to wither, turn brown, and fall. But, when weather cooperates, rich golds, bold reds, and even magestic purples coloring the canopy of leaves over a path through the woods in the Northeast. Meanwhile, on the farther coast, there are westerners. Enjoying the bronzing of tall oaks on the Livermore Hills east of San Francisco.

Exercise E

Rewrite the following paragraph, correcting all fragment errors.

Understanding the very basic science of leaf coloration. This can make observation more interesting. The gradual, but quite dazzling, color changes among the leaves of deciduous trees like oaks, hickories, sumacs, maples, aspens, and gums. Occurring only in America's temperate zones.

And among these areas, the display in the East especially brilliant in its colors of autumn foliage. Exceptionally breathtaking views can be seen by travelers on New England roadway tours. The sugar maples ablaze in fiery red. This incredible backdrop of color awed vacationers for countless autumn seasons.

Exercise F

Rewrite the following paragraphs, correcting all fragment errors.

Tiny capsules of green pigment called chlorophyll. Inside the cell tissue of leaves. During the warm summer months. When chlorophyll participates in food and energy processes in the leaves. Inside the capsules of chlorophyll are. Two other pigments called carotenoids. However, xanthophyll (which is yellow) and carotene (which is orange) are masked during the summer months by the working chlorophyll.

By summer's end, with the decrease in sunlight hours and the lower temperatures at night. The leaves' living processes begin to slow down. Chlorophyll undergoes a rapid deterioration, eventually disappearing. Only the xanthophyll and carotene are left, and the leaves begin their color transformation to yellows and oranges.

Exercise G

Rewrite the following paragraphs, correcting all fragment errors.

There is another group of color pigments responsible for perhaps the most dramatic coloration. Though not as commonly occurring in leaves as carotenoids. These pigments are anthocyanins. Which, unlike carotenoids, are not present in the summer months. Also unlike carotenoids, these pigments not confined inside the capsules of chlorophyll. Instead, anthocyanins are first formed in autumn and appear in the uppermost cell layers. Dominating over other pigments present deeper. The pigments can variously combine. Bringing reds and magentas and blues and purples to leaves.

Leaves containing anthocyanins can offer the must unusual colors and variations. Their combination with carotenoids in different layers of the leaves bringing out the most extraordinary colors. Even leaves on the same tree can appear to have subtle differences in color. Because of slight combinations of their pigments.

Mastery Test

Identify what part of the sentence is missing and needs to be added to make the fragment into a sentence.

    A.   Add a subject
    B.   Add a verb
    C.   Add a subject and a verb
    D.   The subject and verb are present, but it doesn't express a complete thought.

1.   to go on his annual fall camping trip this weekend

2.   every year, for two glorious weeks, he camps

3.   come from their home towns in Little Rock and Pine Bluff

4.   when they were all in college in Fayetteville

5.   the spectacularly beautiful Ozark Mountains

6.   the trees' crimson, orange, and yellow leaves

7.   is a pilgrimage back to their carefree college days

8.   now they all have

9.   is good for renewing their spirits and strengthening their friendships

10.   the chance to rest, relax, and escape occasionally

COMBINING SENTENCES USING THE THREE METHODS OF COORDINATION

Diagnostic Test

Each of the following sentences contains a blank. In each case, choose A, B, or C to indicate which coordinating conjunction best combines the two clauses.

B   1.   There are two types of sequoia in California, _____ they are both impressively grand.
            A)   for
            B)   but
            C)   or

B   2.   One species is called *sequoia sempervirens*, _____ the other is called *sequoia gigantea*.
            A)   but
            B)   and
            C)   or

A   3.   *Sequoia sempervirens*, or coast redwood, grows in thick groves, _____ very little sunlight reaches the ground beneath.
            A)   so
            B)   but
            C)   and

C   4.   _____ are the groves thick and dark, _____ the trees are among the highest in the world.
            A)   neither...nor
            B)   either...or
            C)   not only... but also

B   5.   When I visited northern California, I brought along good hiking gear, _____ I went primarily to walk in the woods among these giant trees.
            A)   or
            B)   for
            C)   yet

C   6.   The bark of these enormous giants can be two feet thick, _____ tracing your finger along its groves is fascinating.
            A)   for
            B)   but
            C)   and

B   7.   The other species is found in the Sierra, _____ it is the *sequoia gigantean*, or sierra redwood..
            A)   but
            B)   and
            C)   for

C   8.   These grow more apart from each other, _____ the bright sunshine can brighten the forest floor.
            A)   yet
            B)   and
            C)   so

9.   _____ they are pointed at the top like cones, ____ they can be broken at the top by storms.
    A)   Either…or
    B)   Not only…but also
    C)   Neither…nor

10.   When I walked beneath the coast redwoods, I felt somehow humbled, ____ I remember feeling the same way watching the crashing falls at Niagara.
    A)   yet
    B)   and
    C)   for

Exercise A

Each of the following examples contains two simple sentences that could be combined with a coordinating conjunction. In each case, choose A, B, or C to indicate which coordinating conjunction best combines the two sentences.

1.   Clouds appear in countless shapes. They can be quite an interesting phenomenon to observe.
    A)   or
    B)   yet
    C)   so

2.   Clouds have fascinated observers for thousands of years. Learning the types aids in weather forecasting.
    A)   nor
    B)   for
    C)   and

3.   There occur in the atmosphere several types of clouds. Clouds can be considered basically to fall into three main groups.
    A)   but
    B)   nor
    C)   so

4.   Clouds are classed mainly according to their appearance. The three main group names are *cumulus, stratus,* and *cirrus.*
    A)   so
    B)   and
    C)   yet

5.   *Cumulus* clouds can resemble white cauliflower crowns. They often appear as rising domes or mounds on summer days.
    A)   for
    B)   so
    C)   but

6.   When rain is predicted, the *cumulus* cloud becomes the *cumulus congestus.* The cloud greatly enlarges.
    A)   but
    B)   for
    C)   nor

C 7. Rain often falls as predicted from the towering clouds. The cloud takes the name *cumulonimbus*.
A) yet
B) nor
C) and

B 8. Another group, arranged in thin flat layers, is called the *stratus*. If this cloud occurs at higher altitudes, it is called *altostratus*.
A) so
B) but
C) or

A 9. Some stratified clouds bring either rain or snow. This cloud is then called *nimbostratus*.
A) but
B) or
C) nor

B 10. *Cirrus* clouds are composed of mostly ice crystals. These clouds occur at high altitudes, at least 3 or so miles from the ground.
A) yet
B) for
C) or

B 11. *Cirrus* clouds appear in the form of delicate fibers. They can also look like brush strokes.
A) but
B) and
C) for

C 12. These wispy clouds can be seen by air travelers. Having a window seat is much preferred.
A) yet
B) for
C) so

B 13. *Cirrus* clouds can also appear layered, filling the sky. These clouds are *cirrostratus* clouds.
A) so
B) and
C) or

A 14. There is another form of cloud that does not fall into the above three classes. This cloud occurs at ground level.
A) for
B) nor
C) but

A 15. Ground level air cools, and water vapor condenses. Fog forms to shroud the ground.
A) so
B) yet
C) for

Exercise B

Each of the following examples contains two simple sentences that could be related with a coordinating conjunction. In each case, choose A, B, or C to indicate which coordinating conjunction best combines the two sentences.

1. The house my college roommates bought is very small. The size of the property and the design of the house make it seem larger.
   A)   yet
   B)   so
   C)   nor

2. The property also has a small carriage house that could be rented. This adds even more value.
   A)   but
   B)   so
   C)   nor

3. Ancient sequoias provide a beautiful canopy of shade. They make the home a private retreat.
   A)   for
   B)   and
   C)   or

4. Marin County is a great place for my friends to live. They both work in San Francisco, just over the Golden Gate Bridge.
   A)   and
   B)   yet
   C)   for

5. Both Maria and Jim love hiking. The house, right at the base of Mount Tamalpais, is in a perfect location for them.
   A)   so
   B)   for
   C)   but

6. I got the chance to see how much they love the West Coast. I visited last September and stayed in the carriage house.
   A)   but
   B)   so
   C)   for

7. They live close enough to the city to frequently enjoy its excitement. The quiet surroundings of their new home allow them to relax.
   A)   yet
   B)   so
   C)   for

8. At home, they enjoy their weekend leisure time by reading and cooking. On Monday mornings, they are anxious to get to work.
   A)   nor
   B)   for
   C)   but

9. Both Maria and Jim teach at San Francisco State. They both find their jobs very fulfilling.

A)   but
B)   and
C)   so

10.   They often spoke of going west after graduate school. They looked for teaching jobs in California, Washington, and Oregon.
      A)   so
      B)   nor
      C)   but

11.   They both urged me to join them. I decided to stay east in Burlington.
      A)   and
      B)   so
      C)   but

12.   I have always lived in beautiful Vermont. I look forward to skiing every winter.
      A)   for
      B)   yet
      C)   so

13.   Maria and Jim love northern California's mild climate. They can still enjoy skiing at Lake Tahoe.
      A)   yet
      B)   for
      C)   so

14.   I went to visit them over winter break last year. I plan to visit them **again next year**.
      A)   and
      B)   for
      C)   **but**

15.   Maria and Jim certainly love their new home. I always have a wonderful time when I visit.
      A)   for
      B)   and
      C)   but

Exercise C

Each of the following examples contains two sentences that could be combined with an adverbial conjunction. In each case, choose A, B, or C to indicate which adverbial conjunction best combines the two sentences.

1.   Clothing can be made from any of a number of cloths created from fibers. No other cloth is used as much as cotton.
      A)   however
      B)   indeed
      C)   instead

2.   So much of what we wear and use is made of cotton. You could hardly go through a single day without wearing or using it.
      A)   however
      B)   indeed
      C)   likewise

3.   Each inch-long length of cotton fiber has about a hundred or so twists. Its softness is among its many desirable features.
     A)   consequently
     B)   in fact
     C)   otherwise

4.   Many household fabrics are cotton. Most sheets, towels, table linens, and draperies are cotton.
     A)   instead
     B)   otherwise
     C)   in fact

5.   Cotton's absorbency and ability to dry quickly make it a favorite choice for sportswear. The twists in the fiber give it a stretchiness conducive to athletic activities.
     A)   furthermore
     B)   however
     C)   instead

6.   The best climate for growing cotton is warm and sunny, with fairly moist soil. Cotton is grown in the southern U.S., India, and the southern part of the former U.S.S.R.
     A)   otherwise
     B)   therefore
     C)   likewise

7.   Cotton seeds are planted in the spring. The plants grow throughout the warm summer months.
     A)   however
     B)   meanwhile
     C)   in fact

8.   As the plants grow, they begin to bud. When the plant is about two months old, it begins to bloom.
     A)   in fact
     B)   nevertheless
     C)   instead

9.   When the buds first open, the flower is white. The flower begins to turn pink.
     A)   instead
     B)   meanwhile
     C)   besides

10. The flower finally turns red. In three days the flower dies.
     A)   consequently
     B)   instead
     C)   besides

11. The dead flower is pushed out on the tip of a new boll. The cotton boll grows to about golf ball size.
     A)   meanwhile
     B)   indeed
     C)   however

C   12.   Over these next few months, the boll continues its growth. The weather conditions need to be
           ideal.
           A)   furthermore
           B)   however
           C)   hence

B   13.   The growing cotton boll is really a seedpod. Inside the boll, cotton fibers form around the seeds.
           A)   instead
           B)   consequently
           C)   nonetheless

A   14.   Early fall comes, and the plants are four feet tall. By this time the bolls have turned brown and
           opened.
           A)   however
           B)   besides
           C)   instead

B   15.   The cotton fibers, now exposed, begin to dry and fluff out. The time for picking arrives.
           A)   otherwise
           B)   consequently
           C)   instead

Exercise D

Each of the following examples contains two sentences that could be combined with an adverbial
conjunction. In each case, choose A, B, or C to indicate which adverbial conjunction best combines the
two sentences.

B   1.   Wool fibers can be made into yarn that is warm, soft, and strong. The cloth made from the yarn is
           highly valued by the industry and its consumers.
           A)   however
           B)   hence
           C)   instead

A   2.   Wool fibers are curly and crimped. The fibers can be made into cloth that is warmer than the cloth
           of many other fibers.
           A)   therefore
           B)   instead
           C)   otherwise

C   3.   Wool's great warmth results from its fine and curly texture. The curlier the fiber, the more warmth
           and fluffiness the cloth will have.
           A)   besides
           B)   however
           C)   consequently

A   4.   Curly texture creates tiny pockets of air between the individual fibers. Cold wind cannot easily
           penetrate the cloth.
           A)   hence
           B)   besides
           C)   in addition

5. A protective barrier of dry air forms next to the body. Comfortable body temperature can be maintained.
    A)   indeed
    B)   however
    C)   otherwise

6. Elasticity of wool fibers contributes to the cloth's comfort. This adds strength and durability .
    A)   however
    B)   in addition
    C)   nonetheless

7. Wool fibers can withstand a quite forceful pulling. When they are released, the fibers spring back to their original shape.
    A)   nevertheless
    B)   nonetheless
    C)   however

8. Other animals can also provide special fibers that can prove just as useful as wool. These fibers are also collected and woven into yarn.
    A)   however
    B)   consequently
    C)   besides

9. The Angora goat's hair, called mohair, is the most widely used specialty fiber. **Much of the U.S. has very suitable climate for raising the animals.**
    A)   in addition
    B)   otherwise
    C)   **however**

10. Hair of the Angora goat grows long and heavy. These goats are sheared twice a year.
    A)   thus
    B)   instead
    C)   otherwise

11. The cashmere goat's undercoat is exceptionally fine and downy. These more luxurious fibers are much more difficult to obtain.
    A)   thus
    B)   nevertheless
    C)   besides

12. Cashmere goats are not sheared. Their fibers are gathered by hand when the goat sheds in spring.
    A)   thus
    B)   however
    C)   instead

13. Each cashmere goat usually yields only four or five ounces of fibers a year. Items made from cashmere can be quite expensive.
    A)   consequently
    B)   also
    C)   instead

B 14. The exquisite beauty of a cashmere sweater is in its softness. As soft as it is, it is also quite warm.
A) instead
B) however
C) therefore

B 15. Wool's overall resiliency makes it a favorite choice for clothing and blankets. A fine wool rug or tapestry can be equally as valued.
A) thus
B) nevertheless
C) therefore

Exercise E

Rewrite the following passage, using a coordinating conjunction to combine the sentences before and after the blanks.

Many Americans are becoming more health conscious. Some of these same people are demanding foods free of chemicals. _____ , and They also desire living in a cleaner and safer environment. As a result of some of these concerns, organic gardening has become popular in recent years. Gardening organically involves a closer connection between the gardener and nature. This method doesn't have to be difficult. _____ , for It centers on only two basic principles. First, the organic gardener recycles natural materials. This maintains the soil's fertility. Then, rather than using chemicals, pest and disease control is achieved with natural methods. These basic principles mirror those found in nature. _____ So Applying these in the organic garden will yield fruits and vegetables that are not only delicious but also healthy and chemical-free.

Exercise F

Rewrite the following passage, using an adverbial conjunction to combine the sentences before and after the blanks.

Chicken tenders are the smaller thin strips of meat that come from either side of the breast bone. These pieces are smaller than the breast. _____ ; in fact Both pieces can weigh less than one-half of the chicken breast. Some people prefer these strips. _____ ; indeed Their tenderness makes them delicious in sauteed dishes. Using tenders rather than the breast can allow for shorter cooking times because of

30   Harcourt, Inc.

the strips' size and tenderness. _____ ;thus This can be most convenient when time is short. Cooking

with chicken tenders can yield dishes both quick and delicious. _____ ; however Nothing compares with the

beautiful presentation of the whole chicken breast over a bed of steaming pasta.

Exercise G

Rewrite the following passage, using an adverbial conjunction to combine the sentences before and after the blanks.

Charleston, South Carolina, is a beautiful city filled with tree-lined streets of cobblestone. Visitors can

explore the antique and boutique shops. _____ ;in addition They can appreciate the city's rich sense of history. There are

walking tours of century-old homes and gardens. _____ ; also Walking enthusiasts can view authentic antebellum

plantations. After a day of touring, visitors can recharge at some of Charleston's fine eateries. _____ ;indeed The

restaurants are among some of the South's most renowned. The rich history and picturesque beauty of

Charleston is a prominent tourist attraction. _____ ; however There are always those tourists who prefer the nearby

beaches.

Exercise H

Rewrite the following paragraphs, using a coordinating conjunction to combine the sentences before and after the blanks.

San Francisco has enough restaurants and pubs to satisfy more visitors with different palates than any other

city its size. Frequent visitors and residents rave about dining in some of the oldest and best seafood eateries

on the west coast. _____ ; but The Tadich Grill, founded during the California Gold Rush days of 1849, is the

oldest restaurant in continuous operation in the state.

The waiters wear crisp white jackets, elegantly starched. _____ ; and They saunter among their well-attended tables

with the same dignified manner the place is known for. More steaming dishes of their famous cioppino

(pronounced *cho-pino*) make their way to hungry diners than anything else on the menu. _____ ; for The Tadich

Grill is known for its cioppino, one of San Francisco's most delicious edible delights. The hearty seafood

stew, full of scallops, prawns, crab, shrimp, halibut, sea bass, and clams, can warm the soul like nothing I have since tasted. No walk can seem colder than down the long city blocks of the city's financial district,

, but

when a winter wind blows cold. ____ When a diner ducks inside the double doors of the Buich building on

240 California Street, an instant warmth rises within.

Mastery Test

Each of the following sentences contains a blank. In each case, choose A, B, or C to indicate which adverbial conjunction best combines the two clauses.

B 1. Exercise is the first step to well-being; _____, it can ensure the success of a low-fat diet.
A) unless
B) in addition
C) however

A 2. Aerobic exercise raises the body's metabolism; _____, food is better utilized for energy.
A) accordingly
B) instead
C) however

A 3. The heart rate stays elevated even after exercise; _____, increased numbers of calories are burned.
A) therefore
B) instead
C) however

C 4. Any amount of exercise is better than none; _____, for real benefit, it must be done regularly.
A) indeed
B) otherwise
C) however

A 5. Exercise benefits are not all physical; _____, exercise also contributes significantly to a renewed spirit and a clearer mind.
A) in fact
B) therefore
C) nonetheless

Each of the following pairs of sentences could be combined with a coordinating conjunction. In each case, choose A, B, or C to indicate the coordinating conjunction that best combines the sentences.

A 6. Team sports can be fun for children. They also teach important lessons.
A) and
B) so
C) for

A 7. Hitting the winning homerun can be glorious. It is really the team's victory.
A) yet
B) or
C) for

8. Children naturally feel proud of their personal efforts. Coaches must work hard to instill team spirit.
    A)   nor
    B)   so
    C)   or

9. All players must focus on the team. Personal achievement must remain secondary.
    A)   and
    B)   yet
    C)   nor

10. Any winning team succeeds as a unit. Each individual player is still a vital part.
    A)   or
    B)   so
    C)   but

COMBINING SENTENCES USING SUBORDINATION

Diagnostic Test

Each of the following sentences contains a blank. Choose the letter (A, B, or C) that correctly indicates the subordinating conjunction that could be used for the sentence to make sense.

1. Tropical plants will not flourish _____ you provide them with water, nutrients, and light.
    A)   after
    B)   unless
    C)   as long as

2. _____ tropical plants grow naturally in warmer climates, people in colder places can enjoy them indoors during the autumn and winter months.
    A)   Although
    B)   Since
    C)   If

3. _____ tropical plants are kept under ideal conditions, some species will even flower to add to their beauty.
    A)   After
    B)   If
    C)   Unless

4. _____ they are taken inside before the first cold air of autumn comes, tropical plants can be put outside for an extra boost.
    A)   Whether
    B)   Wherever
    C)   Provided that

5. _____ they are in the home, tropical plants add beautiful color and texture.
    A)   Wherever
    B)   Even though
    C)   Since

For questions 6-10, combine the two sentences into one using the given relative pronoun.

6.   The concert hall is filled to capacity.
        It has now grown silent.
        (which)

7.   That violinist is the concertmaster.
        He is the youngest orchestra member.
        (who)

8.   The older members have great respect for him.
        They await his entrance.
        (who)

9.   The young concertmaster is a favorite among Philadelphia audiences.
        His mastery is matched by his graciousness.
        (whose)

10.   **The young man's proud mother has come to see her son's debut.**
        She lives in Chicago.
        (who)

Exercise A

Choose the letter (A or B) that correctly identifies each group of words as a dependent clause or an independent clause.

B 1.   more Americans are reconsidering the more traditional views on medicine and healing
        A)   dependent clause
        B)   independent clause

B 2.   herbal remedies have recently gained closer attention
        A)   dependent clause
        B)   independent clause

A 3.   with an increasing awareness and appreciation for the "natural"
        A)   dependent clause
        B)   independent clause

B 4.   herbals have become an alternative growing in popularity
        A)   dependent clause
        B)   independent clause

A 5.   gaining choice over the more traditional pharmaceutical drugs
        A)   dependent clause
        B)   independent clause

6. herbal remedies are appealing to consumers with holistic health beliefs
    A) dependent clause
    B) independent clause

7. with rising costs and increasing reports of ineffectiveness
    A) dependent clause
    B) independent clause

8. debilitating side-effects to many pharmaceuticals can at least make a patient wonder about the possible alternatives
    A) dependent clause
    B) independent clause

9. many are researching herbs and optimistically experimenting
    A) dependent clause
    B) independent clause

10. willing to risk many of the unknown effects
    A) dependent clause
    B) independent clause

11. and willing also to rely on a more "natural cure" for the body
    A) dependent clause
    B) independent clause

12. many consumers are heading to the herbalist and heading off the often high cost of more conventional healthcare
    A) dependent clause
    B) independent clause

13. adding some considerable possible health risks
    A) dependent clause
    B) independent clause

14. information that is known about herbal remedies often equals what is not known
    A) dependent clause
    B) independent clause

15. leaving the entire subject wide open for vast avenues of research
    A) dependent clause
    B) independent clause

Exercise B

Choose the letter (A or B) that correctly identifies each group of words as a dependent clause or an independent clause.

1. with the incidence of clinical depression greatly on the rise
    A) dependent clause
    B) independent clause

2. many sufferers who choose herbals are seeking relief from St. John's wort

A)   dependent clause
B)   independent clause

A 3.   which is used primarily as an antidepressant
A)   dependent clause
B)   independent clause

B 4.   treatments for depression are numerous
A)   dependent clause
B)   independent clause

B 5.   traditional pharmaceutical antidepressants are the drug of choice
A)   dependent clause
B)   independent clause

A 6.   with Prozac, Zoloft, and Paxil being household names
A)   dependent clause
B)   independent clause

B 7.   these drugs have been proven to be effective
A)   dependent clause
B)   independent clause

A 8.   although the high cost and controversy over side effects invites consideration
A)   dependent clause
B)   independent clause

B 9.   many pharmaceutical antidepressants must be taken for weeks
A)   dependent clause
B)   independent clause

A 10.   before significant results can be felt
A)   dependent clause
B)   independent clause

B 11.   trying an herbal remedy like St. John's wort can be another option worthy of consideration
A)   dependent clause
B)   independent clause

A 12.   oftentimes proving to be far less costly
A)   dependent clause
B)   independent clause

B 13.   still, questions remain unanswered
A)   dependent clause
B)   independent clause

B 14.   studies continue to reveal answers
A)   dependent clause
B)   independent clause

A 15.   adding consistently to the controversy of herbal vs. pharmaceutical
A)   dependent clause

B)   independent clause

Exercise C

Choose the letter (A, B, or C) that is followed by a sentence in which either the subordinating conjunction or relative pronoun is used correctly.

1.   A)   Nearly everyone has seen the cut diamonds in jewelry while few people have viewed them in their rough uncut state.
      B)   Nearly everyone has seen the cut diamonds in jewelry as if few people have viewed them in their rough uncut state.
      C)   Nearly everyone has seen the cut diamonds in jewelry unless few people have viewed them in their rough uncut state.

2.   A)   The mineralogist, which is most interested in the gem's rough state, studies the uncut mineral specimen embedded in its parent rock.
      B)   The mineralogist, who is most interested in the gem's rough state, studies the uncut mineral specimen embedded in its parent rock.
      C)   The mineralogist, whom is most interested in the gem's rough state, studies the uncut mineral specimen embedded in its parent rock.

3.   A)   The diamond, which is one of the rarest minerals, grows embedded in a rock as distinct as crystal.
      B)   The diamond, who is one of the rarest minerals, grows embedded in a rock as distinct as crystal.
      C)   The diamond, whose is one of the rarest minerals, grows embedded in a rock as distinct as crystal.

4.   A)   Many mineralogists, which search for the minerals, rarely find diamonds in the original rock.
      B)   Many mineralogists, whom search for the minerals, rarely find diamonds in the original rock.
      C)   Many mineralogists, who search for the minerals, rarely find diamonds in the original rock.

5.   A)   Although efforts at searching for diamonds in the parent rock often prove fruitless, there are four known instances of discoveries within the parent rock.
      B)   Unless efforts at searching for diamonds in the parent rock often prove fruitless, there are four known instances of discoveries within the parent rock.
      C)   Whenever efforts at searching for diamonds in the parent rock often prove fruitless, there are four known instances of discoveries within the parent rock.

6.   A)   The oldest diamond was found in Kimberlite as if mineralogists searched the mine in Kimberley, a region in South Africa.
      B)   The oldest diamond was found in Kimberlite while mineralogists searched the mine in Kimberley, a region in South Africa.
      C)   The oldest diamond was found in Kimberlite whether mineralogists searched the mine in Kimberley, a region in South Africa.

7. A) In the Vilyuy river basin, who is in Yakutsk in the former Soviet Union, lies another source of diamonds found within parent rock.
   B) In the Vilyuy river basin, whose is in Yakutsk in the former Soviet Union, lies another source of diamonds found within parent rock.
   C) In the Vilyuy river basin, which is in Yakutsk in the former Soviet Union, lies another source of diamonds found within parent rock.

8. A) Sometime after 1961, diamonds were discovered in India, which was already known for its discoveries.
   B) Sometime after 1961, diamonds were discovered in India, whom was already known for its discoveries.
   C) Sometime after 1961, diamonds were discovered in India, who was already known for its discoveries.

9. A) Until then the more well-known diamond deposits are found in Zaire, Brazil, and on the West African coast.
   B) Since then the more well-known diamond deposits are found in Zaire, Brazil, and on the West African coast.
   C) Before then the more well-known diamond deposits are found in Zaire, Brazil, and on the West African coast.

10. A) News of the findings in the U.S. was not heard whether the minerals were found in Arkansas, Ohio, Indiana, and Wisconsin.
   B) News of the findings in the U.S. was not heard until the minerals were found in Arkansas, Ohio, Indiana, and Wisconsin.
   C) News of the findings in the U.S. was not heard because the minerals were found in Arkansas, Ohio, Indiana, and Wisconsin.

Exercise D

Choose the letter (A, B, or C) that is followed by a sentence in which either the subordinating conjunction or relative pronoun is used correctly.

1. A) Three small words, declared by Neil Armstrong, whose voice surged from Houston to the whole world, began one of mankind's greatest stories.
   B) Three small words, declared by Neil Armstrong, which voice surged from Houston to the whole world, began one of mankind's greatest stories.
   C) Three small words, declared by Neil Armstrong, who voice surged from Houston to the whole world, began one of mankind's greatest stories.

2. A) The brave pioneers were Neil Armstrong and Edwin Aldrin, and the date was July 20, 1969, a date whose would bridge a vast gap.
   B) The brave pioneers were Neil Armstrong and Edwin Aldrin, and the date was July 20, 1969, a date whom would bridge a vast gap.
   C) The brave pioneers were Neil Armstrong and Edwin Aldrin, and the date was July 20, 1969, a date which would bridge a vast gap.

3. A) The last moments, that must have seemed suspended at the time, lead to sighs of relief.
   B) The last moments, since must have seemed suspended at the time, lead to sighs of relief.
   C) The last moments, when must have seemed suspended at the time, lead to sighs of relief.

Harcourt, Inc.

4. A) "The eagle has landed," was the declaration, whom will ring forever in history.
    B) "The eagle has landed," was the declaration, which will ring forever in history.
    C) "The eagle has landed," was the declaration, who will ring forever in history.

5. A) Man had reached the moon; it was a dream that had held many for centuries.
    B) Man had reached the moon; it was a dream whom had held many for centuries.
    C) Man had reached the moon; it was a dream whose had held many for centuries.

6. A) If Armstrong's words, "That's one small step for man, one giant leap for mankind," will surely be remembered, those first four words somehow more accurately defined the moment.
    B) Although Armstrong's words, "That's one small step for man, one giant leap for mankind," will surely be remembered, those first four words somehow more accurately defined the moment.
    C) Unless Armstrong's words, "That's one small step for man, one giant leap for mankind," will surely be remembered, those first four words somehow more accurately defined the moment.

7. A) The other significant moment was when the two were again ready to blast away from the moon into the lunar orbit as though the third crew member was orbiting in the command module.
    B) The other significant moment was when the two were again ready to blast away from the moon into the lunar orbit although the third crew member was orbiting in the command module.
    C) The other significant moment was when the two were again ready to blast away from the moon into the lunar orbit where the third crew member was orbiting in the command module.

8. A) If the single ascent engine had failed, Niel Armstrong, Edwin Aldrin, and Michael Collins would never have become the American heros they are.
    B) While the single ascent engine had failed, Niel Armstrong, Edwin Aldrin, and Michael Collins would never have become the American heros they are.
    C) Unless the single ascent engine had failed, Niel Armstrong, Edwin Aldrin, and Michael Collins would never have become the American heros they are.

9. A) Lunar observers, who have widely studied the moon, can now be quite certain that there have never been any life forms on the moon.
    B) Lunar observers, whom have widely studied the moon, can now be quite certain that there have never been any life forms on the moon.
    C) Lunar observers, which have widely studied the moon, can now be quite certain that there have never been any life forms on the moon.

10. A) It is probably safe to bet that lunar observation, as well as space travel, will continue when the end of our time.
    B) It is probably safe to bet that lunar observation, as well as space travel, will continue until the end of our time.
    C) It is probably safe to bet that lunar observation, as well as space travel, will continue where the end of our time.

Exercise E

Rewrite the following passage, using a subordinating conjunction to combine the sentences before and after the blanks.

Ann arises in the cold dark and goes to the window. _(even though)_ The early hour would otherwise take a

firm hold of her sleep. A great warm feeling rises from within her. _(although)_ A thick blanket of newly

fallen snow can be seen through the frosted panes. Everywhere, the rural landscape takes on a clean

beauty. _(while)_ Sounds are muffled across the fields. Everything looks so still. _(until)_ The wind whips

up and wrestles the chimes on the front porch. They send out their lonely sound, breaking the

silence of dawn.

Exercise F

Rewrite the following passage, using a subordinating conjunction to combine the sentences before and after the lines.

_(As)_ John was sleeping, warm beneath the wool army blanket. The radio alarm cut in with the

morning weather and travel advisory. _(Since)_ The storm had arrived as predicted. John jumped up

from his warm wraps to brave the cold of his room. Like so many road workers he seems to enjoy

the adversity that snow creates. _(even if)_ The warm covers on his bed can sometimes seem a whole lot

more inviting than the cold dawn. John's sense of duty wins out. _(whenever)_ Snow covers the city

streets, with a promise to paralyze the morning rush. John and the rest of the snow removal crews

arrive with giant plows. _(After)_ The roadways are widened, the plows pushing through to send

discarded snow along the curbside. Intersections are sanded or covered with rock salt. Few

commuters in northern U.S. cities even pause to consider mornings after snow storms to be any

different. _(because)_ Snow removal crews are long gone before the city hall clock chimes 8:00 AM.

Harcourt, Inc.

Exercise G

Rewrite the following passage, using a subordinating conjunction to combine the sentences before and/or after the blanks. Some sentences may have to be rewritten.

I have been witness to nothing so methodic as my father's nightly shaving ritual. _even though_ His pre-

shaving prelude can have its ever-so-slight variations. The doorway is open just wide enough.

_So_ My cat can slither out when the scene gets old for her interest. I struggle to keep my teeth

from chattering in the cold dark of the hall, lest he discover my spying. _Because_ He raises the window

to clear the mirror of steam. I watch as he removes his wooden handled shaving brush from the

metal medicine cabinet. _while_ He fans every bristle to check for some kind of perfection he thinks a

shaving brush ought to have. Then, the lather is never hastily applied. _until_ He first runs through

a complex series of facial distortions and exercises of some kind. The lather is at last retrieved from

the frosted glass shelf above the sink. _provided_ The skin on his face is adequately stretched and

prepared. Finally, the lathering begins. _as though_ The prelude has faded, and the symphony of the shave

can commence.

Exercise H

Rewrite the following passage, using a relative pronoun to combine the sentences before and after the blanks. Some sentences may have to be rewritten.

My father-in-law usually arrives for his holiday visit with us about a week before. _____ I have

always felt for him the warmest regard. Each day he is with us, we do all kinds of fun pre-holiday

things together, like make sugar cookie snowmen with all the detailed trimmings, ride into the

city to see all the Christmas displays in department store windows on Fifth Avenue, and wrap and

tie all our presents to sounds of *A Bing Crosby Christmas*. _____ These days are always among my

happiest. Each night my father-in-law and my son hang more and more ornaments on our little

tree. _____ My son adores his grandfather.

After I read our night time stories, we tuck Sam into his bed, and then we go down to enjoy eggnog by the tree. Getting Sam into bed oftentimes takes great efforts on my part. Later, my husband and his father remain downstairs until long after I turn in for the night. Their hushed voices sooth me to sleep.

Exercise I

Rewrite the following passage, using a relative pronoun to combine the sentences before and after the blanks. Some sentences may have to be rewritten.

Swimming is one of the best forms of exercise. _____ You can do it to exercise without any of the stress of a high-impact activity. It is an excellent aerobic activity. _____ This makes the heart pump more efficiently. _____ It helps the lungs take in more air. Swimming also has the benefit of being very low impact. _____ This is easier on bones and joints than exercise forms such as running or jumping rope. The low impact of swimming makes it one of the best activities for elderly exercisers. _____ They can be seen enjoying rhythmic laps in health club and outdoor pools across the country.

Exercise J

Rewrite the following passage, using a relative pronoun to combine the sentences before and after the blanks. Some sentences may have to be rewritten.

Mention the word "cookie" and almost anyone thinks back to childhood. Practically every American household has a cookie jar. _____ Many of these households have children living in them. (Of course, adults can also be found to be among some of the most passionate of cookie enthusiasts.) Nevertheless, whatever the variety inside the jar, it's certain there are more clanks made by cookie jar lids than by the lid of any other kitchen container. Cookie aisles are probably the most congested at any given time. _____ These aisles are the most popular in every grocery store. There is no food more comforting than the cookie. _____ Cookies can be eaten without any preparation, like the cooking required of comfort foods such as chicken soup or macaroni and cheese. At the end of a long school day, all a kid needs is strength enough to lift the cookie jar lid and perhaps a loving parent. _____ A parent can pour the chocolate milk to wash the last crumbs down.

Mastery Test

Each of the following sentences contains a blank. Choose the letter (A, B, or C) that correctly indicates the subordinating conjunction that could be used for the sentence to make sense.

1.   _____ broccoli florets can be enjoyed raw with light seasoning in a salad, they can also be sautéed in olive oil and garlic.
   A)   Because
   B)   Although
   C)   Since

2.   Broccoli can be a delicious crunchy snack _____ the heads are covered with dark green or purple florets, which are tightly closed.
   A)   provided that
   B)   unless
   C)   when

3.   Spinach is an extremely versatile vegetable that is quite nutritious, _____ washing and de-stemming the leaves is quite a chore.
   A)   while
   B)   even though
   C)   until

4.   When buying Brussels sprouts, choose bright green heads, which are round and firm, _____ these qualities indicate peak freshness.
   A)   although
   B)   unless
   C)   because

5.   _____ choosing broccoli, spinach, or Brussels sprouts, including a green vegetable can complement beef, pork, fish, or fowl.
   A)   Before
   B)   Whether
   C)   After

Each of the following sentences contains a blank. Choose the letter (A, B, or C) that correctly indicates the relative pronoun that could be used for the sentence to make sense.

6.   My friend Mona, _____ house is just across the fence, has a big herb garden.
   A)   whom
   B)   who
   C)   whose

7.   Her biggest crop is basil, both green and purple, _____ grows in the center of all the other herbs.
       A)   that
       B)   who
       C)   which

8.   Mona, from _____ I have learned so much about seeding and growing, has sparked my own interest in gardening.
       A)   whom
       B)   who
       C)   whose

9.   However, it is really my husband, _____, I believe, was my first introduction to the grand art of gardening and harvesting your own herbs and vegetables.
       A)   whom
       B)   who
       C)   whose

10.   Mark, _____ rosemary grew into the size of shrubs, has the "greenest" of thumbs!
       A)   whom
       B)   who
       C)   whose

CORRECTING THE RUN-ON

Diagnostic Test

Each of the following examples is a run-on sentence. Choose the answer (A, B, or C) that corrects each run-on.

1.   Cooking and eating lobster is a joy to many it's a favorite among shellfish lovers.

       A)   Cooking and eating lobster is a joy to many and it's a favorite among shellfish lovers.
       B)   Cooking and eating lobster is a joy to many. It's a favorite among shellfish lovers.
       C)   Cooking and eating lobster is a joy to many, it's a favorite among shellfish lovers.

2.   Lobster must be killed first and most cooks prefer the least painful method.

       A)   Lobster must be killed first; consequently, most cooks prefer the least painful method.
       B)   Lobster must be killed first and, most cooks prefer the least painful method.
       C)   Lobster must be killed first most cooks prefer the least painful method.

3.   There are different ways to do this, many debate about which method is best.

       A)   Since there are different ways to do this, many debate about which method is best.
       B)   There are different ways to do this and many debate about which method is best.
       C)   There are different ways to do this. Therefore, many debate about which method is best.

4.   Some put lobsters in cold water and raise heat slowly lobsters die before feeling pain.

        A)   Some put lobsters in cold water and raise heat slowly, lobsters die before feeling pain.
        B)   Some put lobsters in cold water, raise heat slowly, lobsters die before feeling pain.
        C)   Some put lobsters in cold water and raise heat slowly; thus, lobsters die before feeling pain.

5.   Others prefer the fast drop into boiling water, it's the quickest method.

        A)   Others prefer the fast drop into boiling water; because, it's the quickest method.
        B)   Others prefer the fast drop into boiling water because it's the quickest method.
        C)   Others prefer the fast drop into boiling water, because it's the quickest method.

6.   These cooks believe this is least painful for the lobsters and it's easier for the cook.

        A)   These cooks believe this is least painful for the lobsters, and it's easier for the cook.
        B)   These cooks believe this is least painful for the lobsters, it's easier for the cook.
        C)   These cooks believe this is least painful for the lobsters furthermore it's easier for the cook.

7.   There are other theories one is that lobsters don't feel pain at all.

        A)   There are other theories. One is that lobsters don't feel pain at all.
        B)   There are other theories and one is that lobsters don't feel pain at all.
        C)   There are other theories; and one is that lobsters don't feel pain at all.

8.   Another belief seems the most humane stroking lobsters' backs hypnotizes them.

        A)   Another belief seems the most humane. Stroking lobsters' backs hypnotizes them.
        B)   Another belief seems the most humane, stroking the lobsters' backs hypnotizes them.
        C)   Another belief seems the most humane in fact stroking the lobsters' backs hypnotises them.

9.   Whatever way is employed, the outcome is the same the lobster meets its demise.

        A)   Whatever way is employed, the outcome is the same and the lobster meets its demise.
        B)   Whatever way is employed, the outcome is the same; the lobster meets its demise.
        C)   Whatever way is employed, the outcome is the same and, the lobster meets its demise.

10.   Savoring lobster in a restaurant is one thing cooking lobster yourself is quite another.

        A)   Savoring lobster in a restaurant is one thing, cooking lobster yourself is quite another.
        B)   Savoring lobster in a restaurant is one thing; cooking lobster yourself is quite another.
        C)   Savoring lobster in a restaurant is one thing or, cooking lobster yourself is quite another.

Exercise A

For each of the following examples, choose A, B, or C to correctly identify the example as a fragment, a run-on, or a complete sentence.

1.   The nervous system is composed of countless nerve cells, which are the basic units of this complex system.

A)   fragment
B)   run-on
C)   complete sentence

2.   Nerve cells are called neurons, they are present all throughout the body.
A)   fragment
B)   run-on
C)   complete sentence

3.   Neuroglia, acting as a supportive framework around them.
A)   fragment
B)   run-on
C)   complete sentence

4.   Signals are sent to the brain via the neurons and these signals travel from neuron to neuron.
A)   fragment
B)   run-on
C)   complete sentence

5.   Crosses over a synapse, the junction between neurons.
A)   fragment
B)   run-on
C)   complete sentence

6.   **After the brain interprets these signals.**
A)   fragment
B)   **run-on**
C)   complete sentence

7.   **Messages are sent back through other nerve cells.**
A)   fragment
B)   run-on
C)   complete sentence

8.   These messages can order movement, they can bring muscles into action.
A)   fragment
B)   run-on
C)   complete sentence

9.   It is no wonder the complex arrangement of neurons has been a crucial subject of exploration for brain researchers.
A)   fragment
B)   run-on
C)   complete sentence

10.   The brain is the master of the nervous system, it is the commander of all the body's other systems.
A)   fragment
B)   run-on
C)   complete sentence

11. With some of the primary parts being the cerebrum, the cerebellum, the thalamus, the hypothalamus, and the brain stem.
   A) fragment
   B) run-on
   C) complete sentence

12. Each part has a distinct function.
   A) fragment
   B) run-on
   C) complete sentence

13. The spinal cord connects to the brain at the brain stem.
   A) fragment
   B) run-on
   C) complete sentence

14. The spinal cord, also composed of neurons and neuroglia, acts as a communication pathway.
   A) fragment
   B) run-on
   C) complete sentence

15. The brain and the spinal cord work together, they both comprise the central nervous system.
   A) fragment
   B) run-on
   C) complete sentence

Exercise B

Choose the letter (A, B, or C) that correctly identifies each group of words as a fragment, a run-on, or a complete sentence.

1. The autonomic nervous system, which regulates major organs.
   A) fragment
   B) run-on sentence
   C) complete sentence

2. The top of the spinal cord, connecting with the brain at the brain stem, begins to thicken.
   A) fragment
   B) run-on sentence
   C) complete sentence

3. Known as the medulla, has nerves that connect to the face.
   A) fragment
   B) run-on sentence
   C) complete sentence

4. Many of the body's reflexes make connections through the medulla.
   A) fragment
   B) run-on sentence
   C) complete sentence

5. Such a basic function as coughing.
   A)   fragment
   B)   run-on sentence
   C)   complete sentence

6. The medulla also controls other reflexes that are unconscious, an example is the moving of food through the digestive system through peristalsis.
   A)   fragment
   B)   run-on sentence
   C)   complete sentence

7. Which breaks up food and moves it through the intestines.
   A)   fragment
   B)   run-on sentence
   C)   complete sentence

8. The vital activities of the body – the beating of the heart and the rhythmic movement of the lungs – are also reliant on the medulla.
   A)   fragment
   B)   run-on sentence
   C)   complete sentence

9. Major motor nerves cross at the medulla, nerves on the left side go to the right brain and nerves on the right side go to the left brain.
   A)   fragment
   B)   run-on sentence
   C)   complete sentence

10. With its many synapses, carries messages back and forth between cerebrum and muscles.
    A)   fragment
    B)   run-on sentence
    C)   complete sentence

11. The pons, or bridge, lies just above the medulla it connects the medulla to the cerebrum.
    A)   fragment
    B)   run-on sentence
    C)   complete sentence

12. The midbrain, which assists in muscle control.
    A)   fragment
    B)   run-on sentence
    C)   complete sentence

13. Relaying messages about hot and cold.
    A)   fragment
    B)   run-on sentence
    C)   complete sentence

14. Below the thalamus, the hypothalamus controls the amount of water in the body.
    A)   fragment
    B)   run-on sentence
    C)   complete sentence

Harcourt, Inc.

15. In the hypothalamus, the body's appetite and resulting hunger are regulated, this is a crucial factor in sustaining optimal bodily function.
    A) fragment
    B) run-on sentence
    C) complete sentence

Exercise C

Choose the sentence (A, B, or C) that is not a run-on sentence.

1. A) Home winemaking has been practiced by many people around the world for centuries, its appeal has not diminished in recent years.
   B) Home winemaking has been practiced by many people around the world for centuries, and its appeal has not diminished in recent years.
   C) Home winemaking has been practiced by many people around the world for centuries and its appeal has not diminished in recent years.

2. A) Varietal grapes from the *vitis vinifera* family are preferred by home winemakers they are preferred for their fine European flavor and their optimal sugar and acid balance.
   B) Varietal grapes from the *vitis vinifera* family are preferred by home winemakers for their fine European flavor and their optimal sugar and acid balance.
   C) Varietal grapes from the *vitis vinifera* family are preferred by home winemakers, they are preferred for their fine European flavor, and their optimal sugar and acid balance.

3. A) Various books and magazines are available for reference serious winemakers read these sources regularly.
   B) Various books and magazines are available for reference, and serious winemakers read these sources regularly.
   C) Various books and magazines are available for reference and serious winemakers read these sources regularly.

4. A) All plans are cancelled when the call is received that the grapes have arrived from California, because it's time to make wine.
   B) All plans are cancelled when the call is received that the grapes have arrived from California, it's time to make wine.
   C) All plans are cancelled when the call is received that the grapes have arrived from California because it's time to make wine.

5. A) The grapes are gently crushed and de-stemmed, they are also mixed with sulfites to protect the wine from bacterial infection.
   B) The grapes, which are gently crushed and de-stemmed, are mixed with sulfites to protect the wine from bacterial infection.
   C) The grapes are gently crushed and de-stemmed, they are then mixed with sulfites to protect the wine from bacterial infection.

6. A) The wine is called must at this point it is not yet fermented.
   B) The wine is called must at this point and it is not yet fermented.
   C) The wine is called must at this point, since it is not yet fermented.

7. A) Sometimes it is necessary, it is then critical to test and adjust the sugar and acid content of the must.
   B) Sometimes it is necessary, it is critical to test and adjust the sugar and acid content of the must.
   C) It is critical to test and adjust, if necessary, the sugar and acid content of the must.

8. A) The sugar content is measured with a hydrometer, it looks like a thermometer with a bulb on the end.
   B) The sugar content is measured with a hydrometer and it looks like a thermometer with a bulb on the end.
   C) The sugar content is measured with a hydrometer, which looks like a thermometer with a bulb on the end.

9. A) Too much sugar will result in a strong wine and too little sugar will yield a weak wine.
   B) Too much sugar will result in a strong wine; too little sugar will yield a weak wine.
   C) Too much sugar will result in a strong wine too little sugar will yield a weak wine.

10. A) The acid content is measured by a process called titration, which measures the PH of the wine.
    B) The acid content is measured by a process called titration, it measures the PH of the wine.
    C) The acid content is measured by a process called titration and it measures the PH of the wine.

11. A) We are making red wine; so a PH of about 6.5 grams per liter is desired.
    B) We are making red wine, so a PH of about 6.5 grams per liter is desired.
    C) We are making red wine so a PH of about 6.5 grams per liter is desired.

12. A) California grapes typically lack enough acid a measured amount of acid blend is added to the must.
    B) California grapes typically lack enough acid and a measured amount of acid blend is added to the must.
    C) California grapes typically lack enough acid, so a measured amount of acid blend is added to the must.

13. A) Yeasts are natural microbes that ferment the must they consume the fruit sugars and secreting alcohol and carbon dioxide.
    B) Yeasts are natural microbes that ferment the must; they consume the fruit sugars and secrete alcohol and carbon dioxide.
    C) Yeasts are natural microbes that ferment the must, they consume the fruit sugars and secrete alcohol and carbon dioxide.

14. A) After a week of fermentation, the grape skins, seeds, and pulp are removed from the fermenting wine they are pressed to release their remaining liquid.
    B) After a week of fermentation, the grape skins, seeds, and pulp are removed from the fermenting wine; they are pressed to release their remaining liquid.
    C) After a week of fermentation, the grape skins, seeds, and pulp are removed from the fermenting wine and they are pressed to release their remaining liquid.

Harcourt, Inc.

15. A) The wine spends a year or more in an oak barrel and this gives it time to mature and develop complex flavors before it is bottled.
     B) The wine spends a year or more in an oak barrel, this gives it time to mature and develop complex flavors before it is bottled.
     C) The wine spends a year or more in an oak barrel, which gives it time to mature and develop complex flavors before it is bottled.

Exercise D

Choose the sentence (A, B, or C) that is not a run-on sentence.

1. A) Eating a diet rich in phytochemicals aids in cancer prevention these chemicals naturally occur in abundance in plant-based foods.
    B) Eating a diet rich in phytochemicals aids in cancer prevention; these chemicals naturally occur in abundance in plant-based foods.
    C) Eating a diet rich in phytochemicals aids in cancer prevention, these chemicals naturally occur in abundance in plant-based foods

2. A) Phytochemicals do not act as nutrients themselves, but they seem to have significant effects on health.
    B) Phytochemicals do not act as nutrients themselves but, they seem to have significant effects on health.
    C) Phytochemicals do not act as nutrients themselves they seem to have significant effects on health.

3. A) Phytochemicals occur in all plants however those present in fruits and vegetables may be the most powerful disease fighters
    B) Phytochemicals occur in all plants, however those present in fruits and vegetables may be the most powerful disease fighters
    C) Phytochemicals occur in all plants; however, those present in fruits and vegetables may be the most powerful disease fighters.

4. A) Broccoli, a cruciferous vegetable, is very rich in sulforaphane and interferes with tumor growth.
    B) Broccoli, a cruciferous vegetable, is very rich in sulforaphane, it interferes with tumor growth.
    C) Broccoli, a cruciferous vegetable, is very rich in sulforaphane and it interferes with tumor growth.

5. A) Citrus fruits may help to inhibit blood from clotting, also they may add a flavorful twist to foods and beverages.
    B) Citrus fruits may help to inhibit blood from clotting, as well as to add a flavorful twist to foods and beverages.
    C) Citrus fruits may help to inhibit blood from clotting as well they may add a flavorful twist to foods and beverages.

6. A) Pumpkins' carotenoids give the fruit its seasonal color and, these phytochemicals protect the body from several cancers.
    B) Pumpkins' carotenoids give the fruit its seasonal color and these phytochemicals protect the body from several cancers
    C) Pumpkins' carotenoids give the fruit its seasonal color, and these phytochemicals protect the body from several cancers.

7.   A)   Enthusiasts of foods spiced with chili peppers enjoy not only the peppers' heat but they also enjoy their interference of cancer development because of the phytochemical capsaicin.

   B)   Enthusiasts of foods spiced with chili peppers enjoy not only the peppers' heat, they also enjoy their interference of cancer development because of the phytochemical capsaicin.

   C)   Enthusiasts of foods spiced with chili peppers enjoy not only the peppers' heat but also their interference of cancer development because of the phytochemical capsaicin.

8.   A)   Lycopene, present in tomatoes, seems to reduce the risk of cancers in the prostate.
   B)   Lycopene is present in tomatoes, it seems to reduce the risk of cancers in the prostate.
   C)   Lycopene is present in tomatoes it seems to reduce the risk of cancers in the prostate.

9.   A)   The ellagic acid in strawberries can help to reduce the effects of the carcinogens in tobacco smoke and air pollution, these carcinogens cause genetic damage.

   B)   The ellagic acid in strawberries can help to reduce the effects of the carcinogens in tobacco smoke and air pollution, which cause genetic damage.

   C)   The ellagic acid in strawberries can help to reduce the effects of the carcinogens in tobacco smoke and air pollution and these carcinogens cause genetic damage.

10.   A)   When brewed, tea leaves provide soothing, calming qualities and the polyphenols present in the leaves may also help fight heart disease and certain cancers.

   B)   Not only do they provide soothing, calming qualities when brewed, but tea leaves, containing polyphenols, may also help the fight against heart disease and certain cancers.

   C)   When brewed, tea leaves provide soothing, calming qualities, the polyphenols present in the leaves may also help fight heart disease and certain cancers.

11.   A)   Eating the whole grain—the germ, the endosperm, and the bran—gives the body all the grain's nutrients but eating refined grain supplies the body with only the carbohydrate.

   B)   Eating the whole grain—the germ, the endosperm, and the bran—gives the body all the grain's nutrients, eating refined grain supplies the body with only the carbohydrate.

   C)   Eating the whole grain—the germ, the endosperm, and the bran—gives the body all the grain's nutrients; however, eating refined grain supplies the body with only the carbohydrate.

12.   A)   Diets rich in whole grains may help to reduce the risk of colon cancer, the saponins in oats and brown rice seem to neutralize cancer-causing substances in the intestines.

   B)   Diets rich in whole grains may help to reduce the risk of colon cancer, as the saponins in oats and brown rice seem to neutralize cancer-causing substances in the intestines.

   C)   Diets rich in whole grains may help to reduce the risk of colon cancer as the saponins in oats and brown rice seem to neutralize cancer-causing substances in the intestines.

13.   A)   The lignans in flaxseed are converted by the body to a form of estrogen and these phytochemicals may protect against certain cancers.

   B)   The lignans in flaxseed are converted by the body to a form of estrogen; these phytochemicals may protect against certain cancers.

   C)   The lignans in flaxseed are converted by the body to a form of estrogen these phytochemicals may protect against certain cancers.

14.	A)	Because the mixture of powdered flaxseed and cold water has the same consistency as beaten eggs, flaxseed is often used as an egg replacement in recipes.
	B)	The mixture of powdered flaxseed and cold water has the same consistency as beaten eggs, flaxseed is often used as an egg replacement in recipes.
	C)	The mixture of powdered flaxseed and cold water has the same consistency as beaten eggs and flaxseed is often used as an egg replacement in recipes.

15.	A)	Another health benefit of flaxseed is its ability to lower blood cholesterol, this is because of the lecithin in the flaxseed.
	B)	Another health benefit of flaxseed, which contains lecithin, is its ability to lower blood cholesterol.
	C)	Another health benefit of flaxseed is its ability to lower blood cholesterol and this is because of the lecithin in the flaxseed.

Exercise E

Revise the following passage, correcting any run-ons.

Edgar Allan Poe was born in Boston in 1809, in spite of many of his harsh critics his canon of tales and poetry endures strong for many American readers. To those readers, Poe is the great father of the genre of detective fiction, to them, Poe is a great master of mystery and myth, his work is brilliantly sprinkled with sly references and allusions. Conversely, the critics have condemned the meaning in Poe's writing as unintelligible they argue that if readers accept the role of detective while reading his tales, they only arrive at the author's flaw. Readers can search for submerged meaning and they only find that many of the tales tell the same story.

Nevertheless, Poe's own life was somewhat of an American myth. And what is commonly known about him is of his marriage to Virginia Clemm, his 13-year-old first cousin but his poetry and tales will continue to be widely read and enjoyed.

Exercise F

Revise the following passage, correcting any run-ons.

Born on July 21, 1899, in Oak Park, Illinois, Ernest Hemingway live a quite varied life, ranging from serving the Italians in WWI as an ambulance driver to being a war correspondent for the

Loyalists in Spain. He was a big-game hunter and a bullfighter and finally he was a winner of the Nobel Prize.

Readers recognize bits of his own life in the characters and themes in his novels and short stories. In his heroes are the ideals by which the author himself lived. His heroes bear the wounds of life's battles, they survive by perservering according to a disaplined code of honor. This code of honor means that human dignity can be achieved in spite of physical perish meaning can be experienced in the everyday of human existence.

Exercise G

Revise the following passage, correcting any run-ons.

The writings of Zora Neale Hurston are studied most often in connection with the American literary period known as the Harlem Renaissance, from this period came some of the first recognized artistic, musical, and literary expressions of black artists, musicians, and writers.

In Hurston's well-read novel *Their Eyes Were Watching God*, she is recognized for her creation, in its main character Janie, of a notable contrast to the standard stereotypical images of black women in literature. Readers in 1937, the year of the novel's publication, observed in Janie echoes of the author's own searching spirit, her insistence on self-discovery and self-fulfillment on her own terms and more recent readers can see how Hurston seems to foreshadow in her characterization of Janie the stance of many of the modern American women who would come to read the novel throughout the rest of the twentieth century and perhaps beyond.

Harcourt, Inc.

Exercise H

Revise the following letter, correcting any run-ons.

Dear Personnel Director,

This letter responds to your newspaper ad for a Sales Manager to handle the daily workings of the Pleasantville branch of Tricky's Used Stuff Ranch, I know Tricky's to be the best pre-owned stuff sales organization on the East Coast. The talents I acquired while managing the Beanville branch of Sal's Junk Shop will be a perfect fit for the tough hard-charging culture that Tricky's Used Stuff Ranch has become famous for, my talents are also well suited for your high-hassle sales training program and your reputable Stick-To-The-Customer-Like-Glue Bonus Incentive Plan. At Sal's, I learned the value of interrogating employees with a single strong light bulb hanging from the basement ceiling, and I also learned by spying on employees through 35 cameras and disciplining employees on the sales floor to get superior performance results. I have included several videotapes of my performances you will truly enjoy them. I hope we can meet as soon as possible to discuss my future with your company, I know I can be an asset to such a quality pre-owned stuff dealer as the Tricky's Used Stuff Ranch franchise. I really want to work at Tricky's, this is where my exhaustive talents will lead to boatloads of abundant lucrative sales of used stuff to customers who were never more pleased to be separated from their money.

Exercise I

Revise the following memo, correcting any run-ons.

To: All Sales Associatess
From: Slick I. Amm
Date: December 8, 2000
Re: New Sales Manager

Please give a warm "Tricky Style" welcome to our new Sales Manager Jack Black, he comes from Sal's Junk Shop, the largest junk shop in Beanville. Watch out comrades he really knows how to shake up the sales floor. Customers left Sal's with armloads of junk and slim wallets due to Jack's

unique approach to training sales associates with a military-like discipline they really moved junk.
Jack will be instituting some of his famous techniques here at Tricky's Used Stuff Ranch as soon
as he gets his equipment set up in his office in the basement and I can't wait to see the sales climb
to the top of the charts! Please distribute the enclosed videotapes to our part-time holiday sales
employees and give them an early taste of Jack's successful sales management approach. I am sure
they will be thrilled to be associated with an industry veteran, Jack made such a profound
impression on his subordinates.

Mastery Test

Each of the following run-on sentences is followed by three choices in which the run-on is revised. Choose
the one (A, B, or C) in which it has been revised correctly and makes sense.

1.   Marilyn Monroe was born on June 1, 1926 she was born in Los Angeles.

        A)   Marilyn Monroe was born on June 1, 1926, she was born in Los Angeles.
        B)   Marilyn Monroe was born on June 1, 1926, in Los Angeles.
        C)   Marilyn Monroe was born on June 1, 1926 and she was born in Los Angeles.

2.   Her parents were Gladys and Martin Mortenson but she was educated by many adoptive families.

        A)   Her parents were Gladys and Martin Mortenson; however, she was educated by different
                adoptive families.
        B)   Her parents were Gladys and Martin Mortenson; but she was educated by different adoptive
                families.
        C)   Her parents were Gladys and Martin Mortenson, however, she was educated by different
                adoptive families.

3.   Marilyn Monroe first married at 16 and her first husband was James Dougherty.

        A)   Marilyn Monroe first married at 16 and, her first husband was James Dougherty.
        B)   Marilyn Monroe first married at 16, and her first husband was James Dougherty.
        C)   Marilyn Monroe first married at 16, her first husband was James Dougherty.

4.   Monroe contracted for seven years with 20th Century Fox, she made 15 films in three years.

        A)   Monroe contracted for seven years with 20th Century Fox; she made 15 films in three
                years.
        B)   Monroe contracted for seven years with 20th Century Fox and she made 15 films in three
                years.
        C)   Monroe contracted for seven years with 20th Century Fox, she made 15 films in three
                years.

5.　　In 1950 she got her first role in *Asphalt Jungle* she played a gangster's wife.

　　A)　　In 1950 she got her first role in *Asphalt Jungle* and she played a gangster's wife.
　　B)　　In 1950 she got her first role in *Asphalt Jungle*; she played a gangster's wife.
　　C)　　In 1950 she got her first role in *Asphalt Jungle*, she played a gangster's wife.

6.　　She made *Niagara, Gentlemen Prefer Blondes*, and *How to Marry a Millionaire* in 1953, she became an international success.

　　A)　　She made *Niagara, Gentlemen Prefer Blondes*, and *How to Marry a Millionaire* in 1953; consequently, she became an international success.
　　B)　　In 1953 she made *Niagara, Gentlemen Prefer Blondes*, and *How to Marry a Millionaire*, she became an international success.
　　C)　　She made *Niagara, Gentlemen Prefer Blondes*, and *How to Marry a Millionaire* in 1953 she became an international success.

7.　　After breaking her contract, Monroe met and collaborated with Milton H. Greene and Monroe returned to 20th Century Fox under better working conditions.

　　A)　　After breaking her contract, Monroe met and collaborated with Milton H. Greene. Monroe then returned to 20th Century Fox under better working conditions.
　　B)　　After breaking her contract, Monroe met and collaborated with Milton H. Greene and, Monroe returned to 20th Century Fox under better working conditions.
　　C)　　After breaking her contract, Monroe met and collaborated with Milton H. Greene, Monroe returned to 20th Century Fox under better working conditions.

8.　　**In 1956 she married playwright, Arthur Miller, she stopped working with Greene after making *Prince and the Showgirl*.**

　　A)　　In 1956 she married playwright, Arthur Miller and she stopped working with Greene after making *Prince and the Showgirl*.
　　B)　　In 1956 she married playwright, Arthur Miller, and then she stopped working with Greene after making *Prince and the Showgirl*.
　　C)　　In 1956 she married playwright, Arthur Miller she stopped working with Greene after making *Prince and the Showgirl*.

9.　　She was divorced from Miller in 1961 and she was hospitalized for a mental breakdown.

　　A)　　She was divorced from Miller in 1961, and she was hospitalized for a mental breakdown.
　　B)　　She was divorced from Miller in 1961, she was hospitalized for a mental breakdown.
　　C)　　She was divorced from Miller in 1961and, she was hospitalized for a mental breakdown.

10.　　She never finished *Something's Got to Give* on August 5, 1962 she is found dead.

　　A)　　She never finished *Something's Got to Give*, on August 5, 1962 she was found dead.
　　B)　　Never finishing *Something's Got to Give*, Monroe was found dead on August 5, 1962.
　　C)　　She never finished *Something's Got to Give*, August 5, 1962 she was found dead.

MAKING SENTENCE PARTS WORK TOGETHER

PART I: PRONOUNS
PART II: PARALLEL STRUCTURE AND MODIFIERS

Diagnostic Test

Each of the following sentences contains a blank. Choose the letter (A, B, or C) that will best complete the sentence.

B 1.   Some economists believe that the keys to financial success _____.
         A)   are getting an education, working hard, and not to take risks
         B)   are education, hard work, and avoidance of risks
         C)   are educating yourself, then working, and risk avoidance

C 2.   Pieces of her manuscript were piled _____.
         A)   on the dining room table, her desk, and on her bed
         B)   on the table top in the dining room, under some books on her desk, and her bed
         C)   on the dining room table, under books on her desk, and on her bed

A 3.   The interviewers took her to a conference room, invited her to sit down, and _____.
         A)   offered her the position of Vice President of Marketing
         B)   they then asked her if she would like to be Vice President of Marketing
         C)   to consider being Vice President of Marketing

A 4.   The ophthalmologist and _____ marveled at the baby's cooperation in the eye exam.
         A)   I
         B)   me
         C)   myself

B 5.   When it was time to go home, he looked as if he were trying to choose between ____.
         A)   she and I
         B)   her and me
         C)   her and myself

A 6.   It is quite clear that Dr. Politano is the doctor _____, I was told, is good with children.
         A)   who
         B)   whom
         C)   whose

For questions 7 -10, pick the sentence (A, B, or C) that is most clear in meaning.

C 7.   A)   A man pounds the bar and walks into a pub for a beer named Max.
         B)   A man walks into a pub named Max and for a beer pounds the bar.
         C)   A man named Max walks into a pub and pounds the bar for a beer.

B 8.   A)   None of us thought he would ever come after waiting for hours in the rain.
         B)   After we waited for hours in the rain, none of us thought he would ever come.
         C)   For hours in the rain, none of us thought he would ever come.

9. A) As weeks passed, dirt accumulated on the kitchen floor that no one mopped.
    B) Dirt accumulated as weeks passed on the kitchen floor that no one mopped.
    C) On the kitchen floor that no one mopped, dirt accumulated as weeks passed.

10. A) While studying all afternoon, the hunger caused her to grow tired.
    B) Studying all afternoon, the hunger caused her to grow tired.
    C) She became hungry and tired while studying all afternoon.

PART I: PRONOUNS

Exercise A

Each of the following sentences contains blanks. Choose the letter (A or B) that is followed by the pronouns that correctly complete the sentence.

1. Ralph and _____ else he brings with him can help _____ to the snacks before beginning with the collected coats.
    A) whoever, themselves
    B) whomever, theirselves

2. _____ plans are to sort the coats by sizes first and then to sort _____ by color and season.
    A) His, them
    B) Him, they

3. The idea for the coat drive was _____ and _____, but I must give most of the credit to Ralph.
    A) his, my
    B) his, mine

4. Ellen said Bill and _____ went to pick up the donations from the area schools, then _____ went for sandwiches at Doc's.
    A) she, they
    B) her, we

5. No one is as passionate about local families in need as _____ and their friends; _____ is a cause worth joining.
    A) they, theirs
    B) them, theres

6. Ellen and Bill arrived at the distribution center, asked Ralph and _____ to begin unpacking, and Ellen said that Bill and _____ were going to set up tables.
    A) me, she
    B) I, her

7. Soon Ralph and _____ discovered the abundance of donations, and his and _____ efforts continued all afternoon.
    A) myself, mine
    B) I, my

8. I took all the adult coats _____, and Ralph set _____ to the mountainous pile of children's coats.
    A) myself, himself
    B) mine, him

B 9. My exam schedule that week was lighter than _____, and the stress affected him more than it affected _____.

A) him, I
B) his, me

A 10. After a couple of hours, Ralph said goodbye to Ellen, Bill, and _____ and let _____ out the back door.

A) me, himself
B) I, himself

B 11. Bill was always involved in some type of charity work; Ellen and _____ had worked on the coat drive last year _____.

A) him, ourselves
B) he, themselves

A 12. Ever since Bill began helping with the coat drive, even _____ own closets have been cleared of all those musty old jackets some people keep around forever; his wife is thrilled that _____ is involved.

A) his, he
B) him, he's

B 13. All of _____ admired Ellen and Bill's efforts; no couple's dedication is stronger than _____.

A) ourselves, them
B) us, theirs

B 14. Later, when Ellen, Bill and _____ stopped for sundaes, it soon became clear that among Ellen, Bill, and _____, Ellen is the one who likes the most flavors.

A) me, I
B) I, me

A 15. Ellen says Bill and _____ will hang up all the coats _____ early the next day before classes.

A) she, themselves
B) her, herself

Exercise B

Each of the following sentences contains blanks. Choose the letter (A or B) that is followed by the pronouns that correctly complete the sentence.

A 1. _____ all enjoyed the reunion on Saturday night, and _____ location was a perfect choice.

A) We, its
B) Us, our

A 2. My best friend Jane and _____ went together, intending to meet many of _____ old friends.

A) I, our
B) me, ours

A 3. Our friends Haley and Anna held seats at _____ table for Jane and _____.

A) their, me
B) their, I

Harcourt, Inc.

4. It seemed _____ excitement matched _____, because so much of the class had come.
   A)   theirs, us
   B)   their, ours

5. Back in school the four of _____ were on the soccer team, and Haley's last e-mail said Anna and _____ were playing on the women's team at the Y.
   A)   we, her
   B)   us, she

6. Anna and _____ were co-captains; no one is a deeply involved in the sport as _____.
   A)   she, they
   B)   her, them

7. Beacon Ridge wasn't Jane's or _____ address any longer, as it was _____.
   A)   mine, theirs
   B)   my, theirs

8. Jane always knew that _____ and _____ would live and work in the city together.
   A)   she, I
   B)   her, I

9. Haley and Anna dreamed about living and working in _____ hometown much more than _____.
   A)   their, us
   B)   our, we

10. Of all of _____, Haley was the one _____ life was most well-suited to our small hometown.
    A)   us, whose
    B)   us, who's

11. Anna thinks the town has _____ charm, and everyone seems content as _____ go about _____ lives.
    A)   its, they, their
    B)   it's, we, our

12. Sometimes, however, Anna found _____ wondering about living in the city and the diversity _____ would be able to offer _____.
    A)   herself, they, her
    B)   herself, it, her

13. We had a discussion among _____ about meeting for lunch, then I proposed some plans and asked _____if _____ would work.
    A)   us, everyone, it
    B)   ourselves, everyone, they

14. Haley said Anna and _____ usually had lunch together _____ on Fridays and could meet Jane and _____ next Friday.
    A)   she, themselves, me
    B)   her, themselves, I

15. The date was set and _____ was a day _____ would look forward to because we knew we would enjoy _____.
    A)   she, we, ourself
    B)   it, we, ourselves

Exercise C

Each of the following sentences contains a blank or two. Choose the letter (A or B) that is followed by the pronoun or pronouns that correctly complete the sentence.

A 1.   "Al, ____ did Carl say called about the car?"
         A)   who
         B)   whom

B 2.   "About ____ are you referring, Marcie?"
         A)   who
         B)   whom

A 3.   "I am talking about the person ____ called during dinner."
         A)   who
         B)   whom

A 4.   "Was it the same man ____ called this morning?"
         A)   who
         B)   whom

A 5.   "No, Marcie, the man ____ called this morning was someone with ____ Carl worked."
         A)   who, whom
         B)   whom, who

A 6.   "He is the man ____ wanted to talk to his son before coming to see the car."
         A)   who
         B)   whom

B 7.   "Al, Carl has so many co-workers calling here that I often don't know to ____ I am speaking."
         A)   who
         B)   whom

A 8.   "Carl told me, dear, that it would probably be Jim Sweet ____ would want to buy the car."
         A)   who
         B)   whom

B 9.   "Jim is the man about ____ Carl was talking and to ____ I spoke last week."
         A)   who, whom
         B)   whom, whom

A 10.   "Oh well, Al, it will most likely be Carl ____ will sell the car."
         A)   who
         B)   whom

A 11.   "He is the one ____ is in contact with the most people."
         A)   who
         B)   whom

A 12.   "He's our son, the natural salesman, Al. Maybe he should be the one ____ should be trying to sell the lake house."
         A)   who
         B)   whom

13. "But, dear, Jack is the one ____ knows the real estate market and with ____ we have dealt before."
   A)   whom, who
   B)   who, whom

14. "Our hopes should be for a sale by the end of the year; they ____ hire an experienced agent will sell the house sooner."
   A)   who
   B)   whom

15. "Goodness, Al, about what or ____ were we originally speaking?"
   A)   who
   B)   whom

Exercise D

In each sentence, underline the pronoun once and underline the word to which the pronoun refers twice.

1.   Making fresh garden sauce involves using home grown vegetables and herbs as its ingredients.

2.   The vegetables and herbs are first gathered from the garden, and they are rinsed well in the kitchen.

3.   A deep stainless steel sauce pot is best; it should be deep enough for stirring the sauce.

4.   Extra virgin olive oil (about 4 tablespoons) is poured into the pot; let it spread evenly.

5.   Chop about six or seven large cloves of garlic, and add them to the olive oil.

6.   Apply medium heat to the pot; lightly simmer the chopped garlic until its color is light golden.

7.   Coarsely chop the onions, green peppers, and tomatoes and add them to the pot.

8.   Simmer the vegetables, stirring them gently with a wooden spoon.

9.   Mince the fresh herbs (basil, parsley, thyme) and add them to the pot with salt and pepper.

10.   Simmer the sauce for forty minutes without a lid to concentrate its flavors.

11.   The cook should taste the sauce at this point to judge its level of seasoning.

12.   The cook can then adjust the seasoning to suit his or her taste.

13. The main steps are complete, but these can be varied to the cook's preferences.

14. Tomatoes, green peppers, and onions are the main vegetables in a fresh sauce; however, others, which may be purchased, could be added or substituted.

15. For instance, an imaginative cook could also use mushrooms; they add yet another variation to an old favorite.

Exercise E

Choose the one sentence (A, B, or C) in which any and all pronouns are used correctly, and that is most clear in meaning.

C 1. A) At Captain Tate's they have the freshest fish in New Bedford.
       B) When you go to Captain Tate's, one can get the freshest fish in New Bedford.
       C) Captain Tate's has the freshest fish in New Bedford.

A 2. A) The specials board announces the day's catch.
       B) The specials board announces to one what the day's catch you can order.
       C) The specials board announces to you what the day's catch he or she can order.

B 3. A) The host, he told the woman in red he recommended the halibut.
       B) The host told the woman in red that he recommended the halibut.
       C) The host told the woman in red that he or she recommended the halibut.

B 4. A) One can enjoy pre-dinner drinks at the bar and wait for their tables.
       B) Guests can enjoy pre-dinner drinks at the bar and wait for their tables.
       C) One can enjoy pre-dinner drinks at the bar and wait for your table.

C 5. A) Tonight, everyone at the bar is ordering the halibut for his dinner.
       B) Tonight, everyone at the bar is ordering the halibut for their dinner.
       C) Tonight, all the guests at the bar are ordering the halibut for their dinner.

C 6. A) In this restaurant, they give you a choice of clam chowder or lobster bisque.
       B) In this restaurant, they give a choice of clam chowder or lobster bisque.
       C) In this restaurant, you have a choice of clam chowder or lobster bisque.

B 7. A) The woman in red told the host he had to make a phone call.
       B) The woman in red told the host that her date had to make a phone call.
       C) The woman in red, she told the host that her date had to make a phone call.

A 8. A) "I love these kinds of mints," she told the host while she waited for her date.
       B) "I love these kind of mints," she told the host while he waited for her date.
       C) "I love this kinds of mints," she told the host while she waited for her date.

C 9. A) The hostess she asked the waiters to bring the trays.
       B) The hostess asked the waiters to bring his trays.

Harcourt, Inc.

C) The hostess asked the waiters to bring their trays.

10. A) The second server who went to the bar serves with a smile.
    B) The second server who went to the bar, she serves with a smile.
    C) The second server who went to the bar, he serves with a smile.

11. A) When you are in the service industry, he or she must serve with courtesy.
    B) When one is in the service industry, they must serve with courtesy.
    C) When one is in the service industry, one must serve with courtesy.

12. A) The woman's date finally returned from one's trip to use the phone.
    B) The woman's date finally returned from his trip to use the phone.
    C) The woman's date, he finally returned from his trip to use the phone.

13. A) The host told the couple that their table was ready.
    B) The host told the couple that your table was ready.
    C) The host told the couple that theirs table was ready.

14. A) Once seated, the man told the server, "I would like the grilled halibut."
    B) Once seated, the man, he told the server, "I would like the grilled halibut."
    C) Once seated, the man told the server, "I would like his grilled halibut."

15. A) The chef sent a message that they had no more fish.
    B) The chef he sent a message that he had no more fish.
    C) The chef sent a message that the restaurant had no more fish.

PART II: PARALLEL STRUCTURE AND MODIFIERS

Exercise F

Revise each sentence to correct errors in parallelism.

1. Some people go into cities, do only what they came to do, and leaving as quickly as possible.

2. Others view cities as exciting, and they think they are also entertaining and interesting.

3. When in San Antonio, I love to eat Tex-mex food, visiting the Alamo, and love to stroll along the River Walk.

4. Some people in New York are fast-paced business executives; sightseeing is done by some who are tourists.

5. In New York, the never sleeping city, you can eat really late at a deli or dance at a club that stays open late.

6. New York by day offers you a lot of cultural events and to go shopping.

7. When I go to Baltimore, I go to the Inner Harbor to shop, eat in restaurants, and I love the Aquarium.

8. In St. Louis, the Gateway Arch was begun in 1961 and finished in 1965, and then in 1966 it was dedicated.

9. Portland, Oregon's more than 200 parks are perfect for leisure, and they are good for recreation and sightseeing.

10. While in Portland, some visitors prefer to relax in Forest Park than shopping and sipping coffee in Powell's City of Books.

11. Seattle offers a mild climate, which enables visitors to shop and tour and to attend sporting events year round.

12. In Philadelphia, it is fun seeing the Liberty Bell, to tour the Betsy Ross House, and strolling in Independence Square.

13. Some Philadelphia tourists would rather catch a quick bite from a street vendor than dining at an upscale Walnut Street restaurant.

14. Various tourist guides are available in most cities; visitors can choose sites, while they map routes and take to noting street names.

15. A detailed travel log allows visitors to taking notes, to write descriptions, and record memories.

Exercise G

Revise each sentence to correct errors in parallelism.

1. Jake believes that there is a time to shop and enjoying gardening has its own time.

2. In their marriage, compromise is common, and it is also essential for success.

3. Jake and Lynne are different in their religious beliefs, work ethics, and they also differ in their disciplining methods for their twins.

4. However, their home is tranquil, and it is filled with love and support.

Harcourt, Inc.

5.   Weekends are a time of shopping, tending the garden, and they all cook dinners together.

6.   Lynne's favorite things are playing piano, reading poetry, and she likes to go on bicycle rides.

7.   Jake prefers to play catch with the boys rather than spending time indoors on weekends.

8.   The boys admire their parents, who are honest, very supportive of them, and they are consistent.

9.   The boys study a lot: after school, while dinner is cooking, and they also study in their rooms before bed.

10.   On the weekends they like to play football more than reading or watch TV.

11.   Weekend afternoons are times of ordering pizza, working on model airplanes, and they all listen to their favorite radio station.

12.   Expressions on their faces reflect their personalities: casual, diligent, very contented, and intensity.

13.   At bedtime, the boys pick out clothes for the next day and promptly the clothes are hung on the closet door.

14.   Independent thinking, making decisions clearly, and respect for others are the boys' traits.

15.   Jake and Lynne are proud of their sons and they really respect their values too.

Exercise H

Revise each sentence to correct errors that result in misplaced or dangling modifiers, so that the sentence is clear.

1.   Looking from the plane window, clouds appeared to him as majestic mounds of snow.

2.   As a young boy, his mother told him many stories of her travels.

3.   Then, flying low, a herd of cattle could be seen.

4.   Professor Ming taught the course on Modernism that students dropped in a week.

5.   Returning their textbooks, the bookstore was just a short walk across campus.

6.   Receiving their refunds, the store clerks accepted all the textbooks from the students.

7.   The bookstore manager only could issue cash refunds.

8.   The store clerks could issue the charge credits that were working during the afternoon.

9.   The soprano captivated her audience singing with all clarity.

10.   Taking their programs in their hands, the concert was over at 10:30.

11.   Many opera lovers fantasize about singing one day themselves in their showers.

12.   Hopefully, they will close their bathroom windows before they begin their arias.

13.   Opera goers appreciate operas more, who read the program notes carefully.

14.   Covered with a thick layer of frosting, she knew the cake would dazzle her guests.

15.   To serve a well-made dessert completely delights her.

Exercise I

Revise each sentence to correct errors that result in misplaced or dangling modifiers, so that the sentence is
      clear.

1.   On arriving in New York, the anticipation and excitement overcame Maria.

2.   Having traveled for hours, so many frantic New Yorkers rushing about JFK airport overwhelmed
      her.

3.   Coming from a small village in southern Italy, so much commotion in a big city had never been
      seen by the young woman.

4.   Being only 17 and quite frightened, her luggage was piled like a wall around her.

5. She spoke to a man, but the man didn't speak Italian in a uniform.

6. Maria felt lost until a woman written in Italian showed her a small sign.

7. Maria looked at the sign, but she couldn't the words make out.

8. Then, gazing at her with familiar eyes, Maria recognized her cousin Tilda.

9. Buried under a mountain of books, I had difficulty locating the letter.

10. I finally found it removing the books from the top of my partner's desk.

11. Always being very organized, the letter would never have left my sight.

12. Jackson saw the Grand Canyon driving to California.

13. Born and raised in the East, the West was a different experience for him.

14. He daydreamed of the cold winters back in Boston, sunning on the warm sand.

15. He called his parents every Sunday, being only ten cents a minute.

Exercise J

Revise the following paragraph, making all parts of the sentences agree. Consider elements from both Part I and Part II of this chapter.

This used to be made for them. Pregnant women that worked always quit your job just before having their baby. Things are different in our society today. As more and more families are requiring two incomes, always this is not the case. Some women are keeping jobs after delivery, while some are scaling back to part-time and participation in job sharing is done a lot also. While many women view theirselves as the primary parent responsible for care of the baby, there are some men whose wives may have the larger salaries whom decide to stay home to care for their baby. Having both their parents so considering what is carefully best for them, babies in non-traditional home environments are very fortunate in experiencing the different styles of care often administered by fathers. Whatever the arrangement, it is becoming evident in our society that parenting roles are no longer gender specific.

Exercise K

Revise the following paragraph, making all parts of the sentences agree. Consider elements from both Part I and Part II of this chapter.

New parents whom decide to use daycare for their child must also decide on the specific daycare setting. Some children benefit from a surrounding that is socially stimulating, which means it contains other children and maybe there are a number of caregivers there. Some parents of shy children say you can help the child more by exposing them to other children. On the other hand, sometimes parents believe their individual children would benefit more from a more intimate one-on-one care situation. This is when the caregiver cares for the only one child. Whether the child attends a daycare center or stays home with their home caregiver, the quality of care is the issue. Any caregiver, whether working in a center or in a home, should be warm, compassionate, and the child should be encouraged.

Exercise L

Revise the following paragraph, making all parts of the sentences agree. Consider elements from both Part I and Part II of this chapter.

When a new parent whom must work lives near her parents, another childcare option becomes available. Children cared for by enthusiastic grandparents can have the advantage of feeling a genuine love significantly that can strengthen the bond between caregiver and child. Of course, this arrangement optimally doesn't work in all situations. Indeed, certain characteristics must be present for the situation to work for all people involved. This is, basically, that parent should respect grandparent, and grandparent needs to be nice to parent and respect their views. The most

Harcourt, Inc.

significant benefit that can come from such a childcare situation is an unconditional love for the child, which sometimes comes from only family members. This is not to mention the added benefit to the parents of the monetary savings, as childcare can be a major expense.

Exercise M

Revise the following paragraph, making all parts of the sentences agree. Consider elements from both Part I and Part II of this chapter.

The idea of staying home to care for one's children while at the same time to return to the responsibilities of their jobs has suggested another childcare option for working parents. Telecommutingùworking from home with a connection to the officeùhas grown increasingly popular among parents with young children. The "fantasy" of telecommuting is that it can allow working parents to be in two places at the same time. This fantasy has become a reality with the connection capabilities of modems and e-mail and this is also true because of the existence of fax machines and the Internet. Many supervisors of workers with proven performance are so happy for the ability to keep such valued employees that one is becoming more receptive to the idea of telecommuting.

Mastery Test

Each of the following sentences contains a blank. Choose the letter (A, B, or C) that will best complete the sentence.

1. On a typical Saturday, they are busy washing clothes, cleaning the kitchen, _____.
    A)   and the carpets
    B)   and vacuuming the carpets
    C)   they vacuum too

2. At Mr. Ott's, there were cats everywhere -- on the sofas, in the kitchen sink, and

    _____.
    A)   under the beds
    B)   they were even under the beds
    C)   even three cats under the beds

3. Macy's Christmas window displays are detailed, ornate, and _____.
    A)   festive
    B)   they also were festive
    C)   they looked festive too

4. Kelly and _____ will host campaign meetings at their house on Sunday nights.
    A) she
    B) her
    C) herself

5. I wonder _____ that charming gentleman is in the herringbone jacket.
    A) who
    B) whom
    C) whose

6. Between you and _____, I think her daughter is a very creative child.
    A) I
    B) me
    C) myself

For questions 7 -10, pick the letter (A, B, or C) that is followed by the sentence that is most clear in meaning.

7. A) In a mall at holiday time, an instinct tells one to keep your packages close.
    B) In a mall at holiday time, an instinct tells her to keep their packages close.
    C) In a mall at holiday time, an instinct tells you to keep your packages close.

8. A) The boss said to the secretary that he was a bold thinker.
    B) The boss said that the secretary was a bold thinker.
    C) The boss told the secretary that he was a bold thinker.

9. A) The foreman shut down the turbine, revolving completely out of control.
    B) Revolving completely out of control, the foreman shut down the turbine.
    C) The foreman shut down the turbine that was revolving completely out of control.

10. A) Taking the dog on a leash, the beach was just two blocks away.
    B) Taking the dog on a leash, his master walked to the beach, just two blocks away.
    C) Taking the dog on a leash, just two blocks away, his master walked to the beach.

PRACTICING MORE WITH VERBS

Diagnostic Test

Each of the following sentences contains a blank. Choose the letter (A, B, or C) that will complete the sentence correctly.

1. The parents were called to the school, _____
    A) but they had came earlier and wouldn't come again.
    B) but they had come earlier and wouldn't come again.
    C) but they come earlier and wouldn't come again.

2. The tenor _____ the aria to our amazement at the last two opera season-end galas.
    A) has sung
    B) has singed
    C) has sang

3.   Mr. Holmes just got a new van, _____
        A)   so he lended me a hand moving my supplies to my new studio .
        B)   so he lend me a hand moving my supplies to my new studio.
        C)   so he lent me a hand moving my supplies to my new studio.

4.   If this outfit had been meant for play, _____
        A)   then why was it so ornately decorated?
        B)   then why is it so ornately decorated?
        C)   then why will it be so ornately decorated?

5.   After Todd finishes school, _____
        A)   he traveled to Ireland for a walking tour.
        B)   he will travel to Ireland for a walking tour.
        C)   he went to Ireland for a walking tour.

6.   He studied for many years, _____
        A)   but he doesn't miss any opportunities to travel.
        B)   but he didn't miss any opportunities to travel.
        C)   but he won't miss any opportunities to travel.

7.   While visiting friends in Nantucket, _____
        A)   he went on a whale watch and sees a school of humpbacks.
        B)   he went on a whale watch and will see a school of humpbacks.
        C)   he went on a whale watch and saw a school of humpbacks.

8.   A flight to the Vineyard leaves at noon, _____
        A)   but he won't be leaving until tomorrow.
        B)   but he wouldn't be leaving until tomorrow.
        C)   but he couldn't be leaving until tomorrow.

9.   She wishes that _____
        A)   he were still living in Leeds Point, which is close enough for weekly visits.
        B)   he was still living in Leeds Point, which is close enough for weekly visits.
        C)   he is still living in Leeds Point, which is close enough for weekly visits.

10.   Joseph would be such a strong and wonderful influence on the boy _____.
        A)   if he lived closer to the family
        B)   if he lives closer to the family
        C)   if he had lived closer to the family

Exercise A

Each of the following sentences contains a blank where a verb should be. Choose the letter (A, B, or C)
that is followed by the correct form of the verb that will complete the sentence correctly.

1.   Through the long cold months of winter she had ____ most of her thesis.
        A)   written
        B)   wrote
        C)   write

2.   The boy displayed great courage when he ____ to defend the girl who was being teased.
        A)   rose
        B)   risen
        C)   rise

3. Very often she has too much to ____ well before it's time for her guests to arrive.
    A) drunk
    B) drank
    C) drink

4. The beautiful wool vest that my uncle wore every Thanksgiving ____when my aunt tried to save money on dry cleaning and washed it in the Maytag.
    A) shrunk
    B) shrank
    C) shrink

5. Daniel wisely ____ all the chrysanthemums for the vase in the hall before the killer frost hit.
    A) cut
    B) cuts
    C) cutted

6. Please have the beds ready for them as soon as they arrive; they will have ____ all day.
    A) drive
    B) drove
    C) driven

7. The children sat in a circle around their beloved teacher and ____ about wheels on the bus going "'round and 'round."
    A) sung
    B) sang
    C) sing

8. On those beautiful summer nights at the lake, the evening breeze ____ in the windows, rustling the organdy curtains.
    A) blew
    B) blow
    C) blown

9. The eager little eight-year-olds had just ____ the second half of the game, when the black sky gave up its mere threat and rain began to fall.
    A) begin
    B) began
    C) begun

10. The junior campers had ____ horses every single dry day that summer.
    A) rode
    B) ridden
    C) ride

11. The dress had ____ so much originally, and it should only be sent to a reputable tailor.
    A) cost
    B) cast
    C) costed

Harcourt, Inc.

12.   When he heard his daughter finally come in, he closed his eyes and ____ for the rest of the night.
        A)   sleep
        B)   slept
        C)   sleeped

13.   The hound may be afraid of the vet; after last visit she called to say he ____ her.
        A)   bited
        B)   bit
        C)   bitten

14.   When Felice was in school in New York, she ____ the 400 freestyle for the varsity.
        A)   swim
        B)   swam
        C)   swum

15.   Planes had ____ to the Vineyard all afternoon, filled with people coming to hear Uncle Joe's band.
        A)   flown
        B)   flied
        C)   flew

Exercise B

Each of the following sentences contains blanks where a verb should be. Choose the letter (A, B, or C) that is followed by the correct form of the verbs that will complete the sentence correctly.

1.   "You have a really good ____; you should have ____ playing softball in high school," he told me.
        A)   throw, kept
        B)   threw, keep
        C)   thrown, kept

2.   The toddlers would no longer be able to ____ if the wading pool ____ a leak, and all the water rushed out onto the lawn.
        A)   swim, spring
        B)   swam, sprung
        C)   swim, sprang

3.   Do you think he has ____ running, even though it was academic excellence that he really ____?
        A)   keeped, seek
        B)   keep, sought
        C)   kept, sought

4.   As the bat ____ the ball and his ticket to college was ____, his mother ____.
        A)   hit, written, wept
        B)   hitten, wrote, weep
        C)   hitted, wrote, wept

5.   Nobody ____ if Natalie was expected to arrive at the gala; she never ____ her reply.
        A)   know, send
        B)   knew, sent
        C)   known, sended

6.   If I had _____ that the man has _____ in his shower for the past months, I would have _____ my bicycle over to listen.
   A)   knowed, sanged, rided
   B)   known, sung, ridden
   C)   knew, sang, ridden

7.   Wendy smiled at her coach, who _____ she had _____ her best race and has _____ her title.
   A)   knew, swum, kept
   B)   knew, swam, kept
   C)   know, swim, keep

8.   I _____ she _____ that the red mark on her hand may have indicated that she had been _____ .
   A)   thought, knew, bit
   B)   think, know, bited
   C)   thought, knew, bitten

9.   She _____ me that last month she was _____ by a bee and her foot ached for days; now she _____ her sandles on .
   A)   write, stang, keep
   B)   wrote, stung, keeps
   C)   wrote, stinged, keeps

10.   I had _____ several stories that final semester that _____ me awake for hours the nights before deadline.
   A)   wrote, keeped
   B)   written, kept
   C)   write, keep

11.   Elisa _____ her son a few more die-cast 1950s cars; the whole collection must have _____ a lot.
   A)   bought, cost
   B)   buyed, costed
   C)   buy, cast

12.   The summer _____ by, and the boy _____ several inches in height before he _____ third grade.
   A)   sped, growed, begun
   B)   speed, grown, begin
   C)   sped, grew, began

13.   The disease _____ quickly, and the shock of his sudden death _____ his mother, who _____ nothing of his illness.
   A)   spread, hurted, knew
   B)   spread, hurt, knew
   C)   spred, hurten, knowed

14.   She _____ the newspaper at lunchtime, _____ working at 4:00, and _____ out of her office by 4:10.
   A)   bought, quit, crept
   B)   buy, quit, creep
   C)   bought, quitted, crept

15.   He ____ me back into the kitchen, where my son artfully ____ through the filet with the knife I
       had ____ him.
       A)   led, cut, given
       B)   lead, cutted, gave
       C)   led, cutten, given

Exercise C

Identify if the sentence is active (A) or passive (P). If the original sentence is active, rewrite the sentence in passive voice. If the original sentence is passive, rewrite the sentence in active voice.

1.   The dish of berries was greatly enjoyed by my father-in-law.

2.   He ate them with much appreciation.

3.   They were hand-picked by me.

4.   Only the plumpest, ripest ones were selected.

5.   At home, I sliced and sugared them.

6.   I turned them very gently in the crystal bowl.

7.   I also poured cream over them.

8.   The July afternoon was scorched with heat.

9.   However, the enormous sycamore shaded our backyard.

10.   Its cool shade sheltered us from the sun.

11.   Later, lemonade from fresh lemons was made by my father-in-law.

12.   We were refreshed by the cold liquid.

13.   Soon large storm clouds were seen rolling in.

14.   Thunder could be heard off in the distance.

15.   We watched the storm, in all its glory, from the front porch.

Exercise D

Some of the verbs in the following passage are incorrect. Find the errors and revise them.

That gloomy night, an angry wind blown so hard that the branches of the large oak tree tapped continually at his window. Soon, the small child was so frightened by the storm that he creeped into his parents' room. As always, his parents had been sleeping soundly and hear nothing. As he sat quietly on the floor, by his mother's side of the bed, he thinks he sees a large arm out through his parents' window. At once he start shivering. He then crawl into bed next to his mother, had closed his eyes tight to shut it all out, and awakes finally to the morning sun shone brilliantly in the same sky that appeared so ominous the night before.

Exercise E

Some of the verbs in the following paragraphs are incorrect. Find the errors and revise them.

It seem to her that he could of come to her parents' New Year's Eve party dressed much better than he is. Now she knowed that her parents and the rest of her relatives would be commenting on her new boyfriend's appearance the next day. If only she wasn't always being compare to her sister. Her sister's husband is a doctor and he is always seed in finely tailored suits or freshly starched and ironed sportswear.

Her boyfriend Jimmy could never, or almost never, be catched in a suit. His normal attire consisted mostly of what he referred to as "vintage" jeans and black T-shirts. Vintage for Jimmy meant horizontal slashes cutted in the legs of the threadbare jeans. The T-shirt he wore has its own array of holes, tears, and bleached out spots. He looked more like he was dressed for an alternative rock club than for her parents' party where he would be meeting the rest of her very conservative

family. She wondered if she should of telled him that the party was going to be a bit formal.

Exercise F

Some of the verbs in the following paragraphs are incorrect. Find the errors and revise them.

Even before they begun to date, Kate knowed that Jimmy was a unique individualist. They had

meeted in a film class the spring semester of their sophomore year, and ever since then they are

friends. On their first study date, Jimmy brung her a mason jar filled with every type of flower he

sees growing along the roads he taked to get to her apartment. She had been so charmed by

Jimmy's gesture that she thinks she'll marry him that very day if he asks.

Months had passed since that first date, and together they enjoyed exhibits at the **Art Institute of**

Chicago, moonlit picnics along the lake, and hikes through snow-filled woods at his father's

cabin. At that very moment, in her parents' dining room, she wished she was in those woods

again, holding Jimmy's strong hand. The only comforting thought she had was that as her stuffy

old Aunt Gertrude, in her red taffeta and pearls, was whispering to Uncle Robert, Jimmy sat next

to her enjoying the Beethoven concerto my brother was playing on the piano, and didn't seem to

know anything was unusual at all. Then, she knowed that he has outclassed them all, making a

place for himself wherever he was.

Mastery Test

Each of the following sentences contain blanks. Choose the letter (A, B, or C) that will complete the
sentence correctly.

1.   Uncle Rob is very generous; he _____ me several gifts while he was in Tokyo, and says he ____
        me dinner tomorrow night.
        A)   buys, bought
        B)   bought, will buy
        C)   will buy, bought

2. She believes she _____ a promotion because she is steadfast and diligent, and because her boss ____ her a substantial percentage increase last year.
   A) would get, would have given
   B) had gotten, will give
   C) will get, gave

3. The puzzled look on his face seemed a clear indication that he _____ know the answer, and that he ____ be able to figure it out.
   A) doesn't, willn't
   B) won't, will not
   C) didn't, would not

4. The child _____ back like a frightened puppy when the thunder crashed, and he ____ more frightened as the night went on.
   A) shrunk, will have grown
   B) shrank, grew
   C) has shrank, grew

5. We are optimistic that by Monday morning his anger will have _____ over, and he ____ with us to the business awards dinner.
   A) blown, will go
   B) blew, went
   C) blow, would go

6. Jack wished that she _____ him the kind courtesy of respecting his wishes, and that she would not ____ his parents about their plans.
   A) would give, have written
   B) gives, written
   C) will give, write

7. The school bell _____ just as the last student entered the building, and he ____ across the hall to his homeroom.
   A) rings, cuts
   B) rang, cut
   C) rung, would cut

8. Despite the good advice their parents ____ them, the two brothers _____ college, and ____ west to the coast for the "good life."
   A) will give, are quitting, drive
   B) given, quitted, drove
   C) had given, quit, drove

9. After we finish college, we ____ to Colorado, ____ to search for jobs, and ____ our friends to come join us.
   A) went, began, written
   B) will have gone, begun, write
   C) will go, begin, write

10. The photographer arrived late for the shoot and _____ that the models were gone; he failed to understand how his tardiness ____ the agency the job.
   A) complains, costed
   B) complained, had cost
   C) has complained, would have costed

Harcourt, Inc.

USING CORRECT CAPITALIZATION AND PUNCTUATION

Diagnostic Test

In numbers 1-5, choose the letter (A, B, or C) that has all the commas used correctly.

1.   A)   I heard that their new house cost $250,0000.
        B)   I heard that their new house cost $2,500,000.
        C)   I heard that their new house cost $25,00,000.

2.   A)   Its features include a heated pool, a green house, and tennis courts.
        B)   Its features include a heated pool a green house and tennis courts.
        C)   Its features include a heated pool, a green house and, tennis courts.

3.   A)   On July 15, 2001 they will go to settlement.
        B)   On July, 15, 2001 they will go to settlement.
        C)   On July 15, 2001, they will go to settlement.

4.   A)   To be honest, I rather liked their small condo in Alexandria, Virginia.
        B)   To be honest I rather liked their small condo in Alexandria, Virginia.
        C)   To be honest, I rather liked, their small condo in Alexandria, Virginia.

5.   A)   Who, I wondered, compromised with whom, to agree to the move?
        B)   Who, I wondered, compromised, with whom, to agree to the move?
        C)   Who I wondered, compromised with whom, to agree to the move?

In numbers 6-10, read the two sentences given and choose whether A or B correctly indicates all the words that should be capitalized.

6.   A)   The new house is just outside the city, in Chevy Chase, Maryland.
        B)   The new house is just outside the City, in Chevy chase, Maryland.

7.   A)   On the 19th of july, I will meet them in GeorgeTown.
        B)   On the 19th of July, I will meet them in Georgetown.

8.   A)   The University is having a Seminar we will be attending.
        B)   The university is having a seminar we will be attending.

9.   A)   Ellen, James, and I will eat Dinner and then attend the first Meeting.
        B)   Ellen, James, and I will eat dinner and then attend the first meeting.

10.   A)   On the phone, James said, "we are really looking forward to your visit."
        B)   On the phone, James said, "We are really looking forward to your visit."

Exercise A

Read the two sentences given and choose whether A or B correctly indicates all the words that should be capitalized.

1.   A)   "To err is human, to forgive, divine," advised Alexander Pope in his well-read Essay *An Essay on Criticism.*

      B)   "To err is human, to forgive, divine," advised Alexander Pope in his well-read essay *An Essay on Criticism.*

2.   A)   I remember reading the essay in an english survey course with professor Engleston last fall at the University.

      B)   I remember reading the essay in an English survey course with Professor Engleston last fall at the university.

3.   A)   One of her favorite rabbis used to remind his young students of Sophocles' wise words, "He who throws away a friend is as bad as he who throws away life."

      B)   One of her favorite Rabbis used to remind his young students of Sophocles' wise words, "He who throws away a friend is as bad as he who throws away life."

4.   A)   "Be slow in choosing a friend, slower in changing," rabbi Fein was also fond of saying, quoting Benjamin Franklin.

      B)   "Be slow in choosing a friend, slower in changing," Rabbi Fein was also fond of saying, quoting Benjamin Franklin.

5.   A)   She hails from the midwest where she was born in Morning Sun, Iowa; today she teaches french at a private college in the northeast.

      B)   She hails from the Midwest where she was born in Morning Sun, Iowa; today she teaches French at a private college in the Northeast.

6.   A)   Occasionally, during the Spring semester, she teaches a course on French poets for the English department.

      B)   Occasionally, during the spring semester, she teaches a course on French poets for the English Department.

7.   A)   He spoke with great pride when he said, "My son is in the Boy Scouts."

      B)   He spoke with great pride when he said, "my son is in the boy scouts."

8.   A)   "They had a fundraiser for the March of dimes," he boasted, "And collected over two thousand dollars."

      B)   "They had a fundraiser for the March of Dimes," he boasted, "and collected over two thousand dollars."

9.   A)   My Grandmother often said, "Thanksgiving is my favorite holiday."

      B)   My grandmother often said, "Thanksgiving is my favorite holiday."

10.   A)   "It reminds me," Grandma would say, "of all the many blessings I have."

      B)   "It reminds me," grandma would say, "Of all the many blessings I have."

11.   A)   His Father, judge Minter, read every book he could find at the Haddonfield Library on the bill of rights

      B)   His father, Judge Minter, read every book he could find at the Haddonfield Library on the Bill of Rights.

12. A) Mrs. Minter is fond of victorian novelist, George Eliot; she is reading her novel *Middlemarch* and says she will finish by november 9.

    B) Mrs. Minter is fond of Victorian novelist, George Eliot; she is reading her novel *Middlemarch* and says she will finish by November 9.

13. A) While his family was camping at Lake Hopatcong last summer, Bill finished his doctoral dissertation at the Free Public Library.

    B) While his family was camping at lake Hopatcong last Summer, Bill finished his doctoral dissertation at the Free Public Library.

14. A) "Nothing I can remember," said Evelyn, "is as vivid as the first winter I learned to skate on the Lake."

    B) "Nothing I can remember," said Evelyn, "is as vivid as the first winter I learned to skate on the lake."

15. A) He has lived on Marner Avenue ever since he began working as a clerk at the Boyleston Post Office.

    B) He has lived on Marner avenue ever since he began working as a Clerk at the Boyleston post office.

Exercise B

Read the two sentences given and choose whether A or B correctly indicates all the words that should be capitalized.

1. A) Jacquelyn Kennedy has been regarded as the most elegant First Lady, according to the article in Sunday's *New York Times*.

   B) Jacquelyn Kennedy has been regarded as the most elegant first lady, according to the article in Sunday's *New York Times*.

2. A) The Clerk in the Cereal Aisle commented that nabisco Shredded Wheat was her favorite shredded wheat cereal.

   B) The clerk in the cereal aisle commented that Nabisco Shredded Wheat was her favorite shredded wheat cereal.

3. A) "It has no added sugar," she said, "Nor any added salt."
   B) "It has no added sugar," she said, "nor any added salt."

4. A) Some wisecracker behind me added, "nor any taste!"
   B) Some wisecracker behind me added, "Nor any taste!"

5. A) Mr. Etting plans to drive west across the country to visit Grandpa in northern California.
   B) Mr. Etting plans to drive West across the country to visit Grandpa in Northern California.

6. A) They were in the U.S. Marine Corps together and haven't seen each other since the Spring of 1968.

   B) They were in the U.S. Marine Corps together and haven't seen each other since the spring of 1968.

7. A) Janet's High School reunion is next Saturday night; she attended Brower High School in the late 1970s.
   B) Janet's high school reunion is next Saturday night; she attended Brower High School in the late 1970s.

8. A) She asked her sister, "Are Mary and Joe both going to see the movie at Loew's Theater?"
   B) She asked her Sister, "are Mary and Joe both going to see the movie at Loew's theater?"

9. A) I ran into an old friend, Amy, at the post office on New Year's Eve.
   B) I ran into an old friend, Amy, at the Post Office on New Year's eve.

10. A) Ted has an appointment with a pediatric ophthalmologist named Dr. Wesler.
    B) Ted has an appointment with a Pediatric Ophthalmologist named Dr. Wesler.

11. A) "I went to see the Doctor last February around Presidents' Day."
    B) "I went to see the doctor last February around Presidents' Day."

12. A) She agreed, "Chapel Hill, North Carolina is a beautiful college town."
    B) She agreed, "chapel Hill, North Carolina is a beautiful College town."

13. A) John's class is visiting the Franklin Institute, which has always been one of my favorite science museums.
    B) John's class is visiting the Franklin Institute, which has always been one of my favorite Science Museums.

14. A) He said to me when he called, "We had a great time yesterday at the basketball game."
    B) He said to me when he called, "we had a great time yesterday at the Basketball game."

15. A) "Yes," I agreed with him, "it was wonderful to relive those memories from the old university days."
    B) "Yes," I agreed with him, "It was wonderful to relive those memories from the old University days."

Exercise C

Read the two sentences given and choose whether A or B correctly indicates all the words that should be capitalized.

1. A) Tom loves boating on the Chesapeake Bay.
   B) Tom loves Boating on the Chesapeake bay.

2. A) While eating dinner on the deck, he remarks to Mary, "isn't this the life!"
   B) While eating dinner on the deck, he remarks to Mary, "Isn't this the life!"

3. A) The four months he loves to travel are September, October, May, and June.
   B) The four Months he loves to travel are September, October, May, and June

4. A) He loves living on the Coast, which is much different than the midwest.
   B) He loves living on the coast, which is much different than the Midwest.

5. A) His daughter also loves the east, where she attends College in Boston.
   B) His daughter also loves the East, where she attends college in Boston.

Harcourt, Inc.

6.   A)   She loves the City, and she goes to Fenway park during Baseball Season.

       B)   She loves the city, and she goes to Fenway Park during baseball season.

7.   A)   She often remarks, "There is nothing quite like a Red Sox game."

       B)   She often remarks, "there is nothing quite like a Red Sox Game."

8.   A)   Tom's son lives in Los Angeles, where he is a Dodgers fan.

       B)   Tom's son lives in los Angeles, where he is a Dodgers Fan.

9.   A)   Tom's son works at UCLA; he teaches Spanish and Portuguese.

       B)   Tom's son works at UCLA; He teaches spanish and portuguese.

10.   A)   He lives just outside the city in Orange county.

       B)   He lives just outside the city in Orange County.

11.   A)   Tom met both his children over Christmas Vacation in Carson city.

       B)   Tom met both his children over Christmas vacation in Carson City.

12.   A)   All Three had read the book *Winter Pines* and discussed it at the Airport Lounge.

       B)   All three had read the book *Winter Pines* and discussed it at the airport lounge.

13.   A)   They all spent two glorious weeks skiing in Sun Valley.

       B)   They all spent two glorious weeks skiing in sun valley.

14.   A)   Then vacation ended, and his son flew west, while his daughter flew east.

       B)   Then Vacation ended, and his son flew West, while his daughter flew East.

15.   A)   Tom rented a car; he drove northwest to Spokane.

       B)   Tom rented a car; he drove NorthWest to Spokane.

Exercise D

Read the two sentences given and choose whether A or B correctly indicates all the words that should be capitalized.

1.   A)   Her two daughters, Allison and June, were born in May.

       B)   Her two daughters, Allison and June, were born in may.

2.   A)   The trees' colors are a stark contrast against the gray Autumn sky.

       B)   The trees' colors are a stark contrast against the gray autumn sky.

3.   A)   On the lawn of the Governor's Mansion proudly waves the state flag.

       B)   On the lawn of the Governor's Mansion proudly waves the State Flag.

4.   A)   By noon they should reach the Canadian Border.

       B)   By noon they should reach the Canadian border.

5.   A)   She's lived on the shores of both the Arkansas and Mississippi Rivers.

       B)   She's lived on the shores of both the Arkansas and Mississippi rivers.

6. A)   That beautiful old Bank Building dates back to the Civil war.
    B)   That beautiful old bank building dates back to the Civil War.

7. A)   The Canadian woman renewed her passport.
    B)   The Canadian Woman renewed her passport.

8. A)   "She certainly looked nervous," Ike said, When the Judge walked in."
    B)   "She certainly looked nervous," Ike said, when the judge walked in."

9. A)   My uncle always said, "Try to treat everyone fairly."
    B)   My Uncle always said, "try to treat everyone fairly."

10. A)   That tall professor teaches Spanish at the university.
    B)   That tall Professor teaches Spanish at the University.

11. A)   She has all her accounts at Equity Bank on First Street.
    B)   She has all her accounts at Equity bank on First Street.

12. A)   While we toured Montecello, Jefferson's home, she read *The Great Gatsby*.
    B)   While we toured Montecello, Jefferson's Home, she read *the Great Gatsby*.

13. A)   He told me that he received his M.A. degree last spring.
    B)   He told me that he received his M.A. Degree last Spring.

14. A)   A funny movie was made about Groundhog Day.
    B)   A funny movie was made about Groundhog day.

15. A)   We must cross the river and go through the woods to get to grandmother's.
    B)   We must cross the river and go through the woods to get to Grandmother's.

Exercise E

Choose the letter (A, B, or C) that is followed by a sentence that includes all the commas that should be used.

1. A)   "I do believe," said the enthusiastic professor, "you will appreciate our next novel by William Faulkner."
    B)   "I do believe" said the enthusiastic professor, "you will appreciate, our next novel by William Faulkner."
    C)   "I do believe," said the enthusiastic professor "you will appreciate our next novel by William Faulkner."

2. A)   "*The Sound and the Fury,* is one of Faulkner's best known works," she told the class, "published in 1929."
    B)   "*The Sound and the Fury* is one of Faulkner's best known works," she told the class, "published in 1929."
    C)   "*The Sound and the Fury* is one of Faulkner's best known works," she told the class "published in 1929."

3. A) "In this novel we see the Compsons again," she told the students "in all their dysfunction."
   B) "In this novel, we see the Compsons again," she told the students, "in all their dysfunction."
   C) "In this novel, we see the Compsons again" she told the students, "in all their dysfunction."

4. A) "Through much of Faulkner the author examines the sorrows of fathers and sons, and, he reveals the disadvantage and restlessness of mothers and daughters."
   B) "Through much of Faulkner, the author examines the sorrows of fathers and sons, and he reveals the disadvantage, and restlessness, of mothers and daughters."
   C) "Through much of Faulkner, the author examines the sorrows of fathers and sons, and he reveals the disadvantage and restlessness of mothers and daughters."

5. A) Female students in the class who greatly outnumbered the males, commented on the author's characterization of Caddy Compson.
   B) Female students in the class, who greatly outnumbered the males, commented, on the author's characterization of Caddy Compson.
   C) Female students in the class, who greatly outnumbered the males, commented on the author's characterization of Caddy Compson.

6. A) "It seems," said Janet sitting in the third row, "that Caddy was really the most resourceful and energetic of all the Compson children."
   B) "It seems" said Janet, sitting in the third row, "that Caddy was really the most resourceful, and energetic of all the Compson children."
   C) "It seems," said Janet, sitting in the third row, "that Caddy was really the most resourceful and energetic of all the Compson children."

7. A) Then Jim remarked, "Yet, it was Quentin, who was given the chance, to go to Harvard."
   B) Then, Jim remarked, "Yet, it was Quentin, who, was given the chance to go to Harvard."
   C) Then, Jim remarked, "Yet, it was Quentin who was given the chance to go to Harvard."

8. A) "I believe, you've both hit on an important issue, for many of Faulkner's readers," said Professor Neidler.
   B) "I believe you've both hit on an important issue for many of Faulkner's readers," said Professor Neidler.
   C) "I believe you've both hit on an important issue, for many of Faulkner's readers" said Professor Neidler.

9. A) "Education doesn't seem to be a choice for Faulkner's female characters," she continued, "No wonder females like Caddy, become dissatisfied, searching for outlets as she did."
   B) "Education doesn't seem to be a choice for Faulkner's female characters," she continued. "No wonder females, like Caddy become dissatisfied, searching for outlets, as she, did."
   C) "Education doesn't seem to be a choice for Faulkner's female characters," she continued. "No wonder females like Caddy become dissatisfied, searching for outlets as she did."

10. A) "Instead, female characters like Dilsey, who exemplify selfless devotion to others, are the females who endure, and this theme has opened the door for feminist critics."
    B) "Instead, female characters like Dilsey, who exemplify selfless devotion to others, are the females who endure, and this theme has opened the door for feminist critics."
    C) "Instead, female characters like Dilsey, who exemplify selfless devotion to others, are the females who endure, and this theme has opened the door for feminist critics."

Exercise F

Choose the letter (A, B, or C) that is followed by a sentence that includes all the commas that should be used.

1.   A)   F. Scott Fitzgerald, whose most widely read novel, is *The Great Gatsby*, is often studied along with the works of Ernest Hemingway, Gertrude Stein, and other American authors of the 1920s and 1930s.

     B)   F. Scott Fitzgerald, whose most widely read novel is *The Great Gatsby*, is often studied along with the works of Ernest Hemingway, Gertrude Stein, and other American authors of the 1920s and 1930s.

     C)   F. Scott Fitzgerald whose most widely read novel is *The Great Gatsby*, is often studied along with the works of Ernest Hemingway, Gertrude Stein, and other American authors of the 1920s and 1930s.

2.   A)   From Fitzgerald's main character, Jay Gatsby, readers see love that is destructive, love that undoes the man with its tenderness.

     B)   From Fitzgerald's main character, Jay Gatsby, readers see, love that is destructive, love that undoes the man with its tenderness.

     C)   From Fitzgerald's main character, Jay Gatsby, readers, see love that is destructive, love that undoes the man with its tenderness.

3.   A)   *The Great Gatsby* like very few other American novels retains its importance, even after three quarters of a century.

     B)   *The Great Gatsby* like very few other American novels, retains its importance, even after three quarters of a century.

     C)   *The Great Gatsby,* like very few other American novels, retains its importance, even after three quarters of a century.

4.   A)   Even though some readers have charged, Gatsby's character as being less than credible, the incredible significance he implies seems timeless.

     B)   Even though some readers have charged Gatsby's character as being less than credible, the incredible significance he implies seems timeless.

     C)   Even though some readers have charged Gatsby's character as being less than credible the incredible significance he implies seems timeless.

5.   A)   Gatsby can be said to symbolize America itself, with America building itself upon a dream, the "American Dream."

     B)   Gatsby, can be said to symbolize America itself, with America building itself, upon a dream, the "American Dream."

     C)   Gatsby can be said to symbolize America itself, with America building itself upon a dream the "American Dream."

6.   A)   Although the novel can be read as an exploration of the American Dream in the face of great adversity, at its depths is the theme of reality and its relation to illusion.

     B)   Although the novel can be read as an exploration of the American Dream in the face of great adversity at its depths is the theme of reality and its relation to illusion.

     C)   Although, the novel can be read as an exploration of the American Dream in the face of great adversity, at its depths is the theme of reality and its relation to illusion.

Harcourt, Inc.

7.   A)   The author however, seems to suggest that the reality is embodied in Gatsby, that reality is a spiritual thing.

      B)   The author however seems to suggest, that the reality is embodied in Gatsby, that reality is a spiritual thing.

      C)   The author, however, seems to suggest that the reality is embodied in Gatsby, that reality is a spiritual thing.

8.   A)   The author implies that, for Gatsby reality becomes what one believes, and, that belief becomes who one is.

      B)   The author, implies that, for Gatsby, reality becomes what one believes, and that belief, becomes who one is.

      C)   The author implies that, for Gatsby, reality becomes what one believes, and that belief becomes who one is.

9.   A)   Gatsby, became the man who stood at the door of his mansion, wishing his guests a good night; for the reader, this is a reality.

      B)   Gatsby became the man who stood at the door of his mansion, wishing his guests a good night; for the reader, this is a reality.

      C)   Gatsby became the man, who stood at the door of his mansion, wishing his guests a good night; for the reader, this, is a reality.

10.   A)   Gatsby's union with Daisy, in spite of her marriage to Tom, is the only reality he knows, for her responsibility to her marriage is hers, and not even his concern.

      B)   Gatsby's union with Daisy in spite of her marriage to Tom, is the only reality he knows, for her responsibility to her marriage is hers, and not even his concern.

      C)   Gatsby's union with Daisy in spite of her marriage to Tom, is the only reality he knows, for her responsibility to her marriage is hers and not even his concern.

11.   A)   The novel's illusion for so many readers, is embodied in the characterization of Daisy, in her own hollow debutante life of meaninglessness.

      B)   The novel's illusion, for, so many readers, is embodied in the characterization of Daisy, in her own hollow debutante life of meaninglessness.

      C)   The novel's illusion, for so many readers, is embodied in the characterization of Daisy, in her own hollow debutante life of meaninglessness.

12.   A)   The author illustrates this hollowness of Daisy, this inability she has for understanding consequence, in her indifference toward the death under the tires of the car she drove.

      B)   The author illustrates this hollowness of Daisy, this inability she has for understanding consequence in her indifference toward the death, under the tires of the car she drove.

      C)   The author illustrates this hollowness of Daisy, this inability, she has for understanding consequence, in her indifference toward the death under the tires, of the car she drove.

13.   A)   These same readers notice how, for Gatsby, Daisy does not exist in reality in herself but, rather as a green light beckoning Gatsby into his vision.

      B)   These same readers notice how, for Gatsby, Daisy does not exist in reality in herself, but rather as a green light beckoning Gatsby into his vision.

      C)   These same readers notice, how, for Gatsby, Daisy does not exist in reality in herself, but, rather as a green light beckoning Gatsby into his vision.

14.   A)   Tragically, Gatsby's failure to discriminate between reality and illusion brings about his death, an incident fleshly concrete in reality.

      B)   Tragically, Gatsby's failure to discriminate between reality and illusion, brings about his death, an incident fleshly concrete in reality.

C) Tragically, Gatsby's failure, to discriminate between reality and illusion brings about his death, an incident fleshly concrete in reality.

15. A) In the end, however, Gatsby, in all his blindness and ignorance of reality-based America, is the character for whom the reader holds hope.

B) In the end, however, Gatsby in all his blindness and ignorance of reality-based America, is the character for whom the reader holds hope.

C) In the end, however, Gatsby in all his blindness and ignorance of reality-based America is the character for whom the reader holds hope.

Exercise G

Choose the letter (A, B, or C) that is followed by a sentence in which all the punctuation is used correctly.

1. A) "The reward of a thing well done," said American author, Ralph Waldo Emerson, "is to have done it."

B) "The reward of a thing well done" said American author, Ralph Waldo Emerson, "is to have done it."

C) "The reward of a thing well done," said American author Ralph Waldo Emerson, "is to have done it."

2. A) I demand sir an apology.
B) I demand, sir, an apology.
C) I demand sir, an apology.

3. A) In the Northern Hemisphere, observers can view, the breathtaking celestial hues of the aurora borealis.

B) In the Northern Hemisphere, observers can view the breathtaking celestial hues of the aurora borealis.

C) In the Northern Hemisphere, observers can view the breathtaking, celestial hues of the aurora borealis.

4. A) The light "streamers" are visible in a zone surrounding the north magnetic pole.
B) The light "streamers" are, visible in a zone surrounding the north, magnetic pole.
C) The light "streamers" are visible in a zone surrounding the north, magnetic, pole.

5. A) Aurora australis the southern lights glow brightly in the Southern Hemisphere.
B) Aurora australis, the southern lightsùglow brightly in the Southern Hemisphere.
C) Aurora australis the southern lightsùglow brightly in the Southern Hemisphere.

6. A) Avid readers believe Bacon's words: "Some books are to be tasted, others to be swallowed, and some few to be chewed and digested."

B) Avid readers believe Bacon's words, "Some books are to be tasted, others to be swallowed, and some few to be chewed and digested."

C) Avid readers believe Bacon's words; "Some books are to be tasted, others to be swallowed, and some few to be chewed and digested."

7. A) *Great Expectations,* one of Dickens' most well read novels, is my favorite.
B) *Great Expectations,* one of Dickens most well read novels is my favorite.
C) Great Expectations one of Dickens' most well read novels, is my favorite.

8. A) The author's main character, Pip, comes to understand true friendship; this comes to him as a difficult lesson.
    B) The author's main character, Pip, comes to understand true friendship, this comes to him as a difficult lesson.
    C) The author's main character Pip, comes to understand true friendship; this comes to him as a difficult lesson.

9. A) The stern professor reiterated, "I was'nt being facetious when I said I wouldn't accept late essays."
    B) The stern professor reiterated, "I wasn't being facetious when I said I wouldn't accept late essays."
    C) The stern professor reiterated, "I wasn't being facetious when I said I would'nt accept late essays."

10. A) As a result, all the student's essays were submitted on time.
    B) As a result, all the students essays were submitted on time.
    C) As a result, all the students' essays were submitted on time.

11. A) "All pages need to be stapled," he warned, "otherwise I'll have 1000 loose pages."
    B) "All pages need to be stapled," he warned, "otherwise I'll have 1,000 loose pages."
    C) "All pages need to be stapled," he warned, "otherwise I'll have 10,00 loose pages."

12. A) "All quotes must come from larger newspapers like, The New York Times and The Washington Post."
    B) "All quotes' must come from larger newspapers, like *The New York Times* and *The Washington Post.*"
    C) "All quotes must come from larger newspapers, like *The New York Times* and *The Washington Post.*"

13. A) She takes the following courses: Milton's Epics, Shakespeare's Comedies, and Hemingway's Novels.
    B) She takes the following courses; Milton's Epics, Shakespeares Comedies, and Hemingway's Novels.
    C) She takes the following courses, Milton's Epics, Shakespears' Comedies', and Hemingway's Novels.

14. A) Her first essay for her Hemingway course was based on a critic's book titled *Jake Barnes: Wounded Hero.*
    B) Her first essay for her Hemingway course was based on a critics' book titled *Jake Barnes: Wounded Hero.*
    C) Her first essay for her Hemingway course was based on a critic's book titled *Jake Barnes, Wounded Hero.*

15. A) Ernest Hemingway, 1899-1961, carried the theme of the wounded hero through many of his works.
    B) Ernest Hemingway (1899-1961) carried the theme of the wounded hero through many of his works.
    C) Ernest Hemingway, 1899-1961 carried the theme of the wounded hero through many of his works.

Exercise H

Read the following paragraph and insert the correct capitalization and marks of punctuation wherever they are needed.

The Harlem renaissance has come to be noted for the resurgence of African-american art. Literature, knowledge, and the arts of African-americans, who had already gained respect for their works in Europe had finally found an open door at home in the United states. Poets, writers, musicians, intellectuals, and entrepreneurs had found a place for themselves. In the 1920s, Harlem New York became a fertile cultural center that fostered and stimulated the arts of so many. Musicians such as Duke Ellington, Louis Armstrong and Eubie Blake, just to name a very few, joined their musical expression with the written expression of writers such as Langston Hughes, Dorothy West, Zora Neale Hurston and Countee Cullen. Visual arts and theater depicted the political social, and economic conditions of being black in America. The time period remains one of the most uplifting to African-Americans as artists.

Exercise I

Read the following paragraphs and insert the correct capitalization and marks of punctuation wherever they are needed.

Equally as significant as the pasta craze of the 1980s' is todays rice popularity. Traditionally the availability of rice in american supermarkets was either plain white rice or converted rice. Todays consumers can choose from many more varieties. Rice enthusiasts can purchase from a growing range of rices thai Jasmine rice , California Wehani, japanese rice, Louisiana pecan, black rice, red rice, and short- and long-grain sticky rice.

There are countless strains of rice varieties world-wide. Most of these originated in East asia where most of the worlds rice is still raised. However rice can be grown on almost any Continent in radically diverse environments. For example rice can grow in flooded tropical paddies or in irrigated deserts. It is the diversity of these growing conditions, as well as the difference in the seeds themselves that account for the distinct color flavor, and aroma of rices.

Exercise J

Read the following paragraph and insert the correct capitalization and marks of punctuation wherever they are needed.

J.d. Salinger was born Jerome David Salinger in New york city on January, 1, 1919. He attended Valley Forge Military academy, in Pennsylvania and he graduated in 1936. After his draft into the United States army, in 1942 and discharge in 1945 he began publishing his short stories regularly in some of the bigger magazines like the *Saturday Evening Post, Esquire,* and the *New Yorker.* His publishing career became most defined by a long relationship with the *New Yorker,* beginning in the late 1940s. Then in 1951 his novel *The Catcher in the Rye* was published and becomes the work that Salinger is most well known for today.

Exercise K

Read the following paragraph and insert the correct capitalization and marks of punctuation wherever they are needed.

Laura my friend roberts maternal Grandmother, was known to him as a simple woman who took care of her husband and six children while at the same time she cared for three children from her neighborhood. She always seemed to honor nothing more than the ten commandments, her husband, and her children. These things, she often said to him, are the things that matter. She took great pride in her home and in her property and she held cleanliness and organization in high regard. She made all of her childrens clothing and to this day I have never seen such careful detail such precision. Robert inherited his grandmothers' cedar chest after she died last Fall and along with countless old photos, Birthday Cards, and past issues of *Ladies Home journal*, some of his

mothers' school dresses are still inside wrapped neatly in tissue.

Mastery Test

In numbers 1-5, choose the letter (A, B, or C) that has all the commas used correctly.

1.   A)   As it turned out, Friday was a cold rainy day.
       B)   As it turned out, Friday was a cold, rainy day.
       C)   As it turned out Friday was a cold, rainy day.

2.   A)   Cats can be very warm, comforting, and affectionate.
       B)   Cats can be very warm comforting and affectionate.
       C)   Cats can be very warm comforting, and affectionate.

3.   A)   Mrs. Eng was overjoyed, for her daughter returned home with $1,000,000.
       B)   Mrs. Eng was overjoyed for her daughter, returned home with $1,000000.
       C)   Mrs. Eng was overjoyed for her daughter returned home with $10,000,00.

4.   A)   Tulsa, Oklahoma, her hometown, is the location of the sales meeting.
       B)   Tulsa Oklahoma, her hometown, is the location of the sales meeting.
       C)   Tulsa, Oklahoma her hometown, is the location of the sales meeting.

5.   A)   "I imagine," he said "you will want dinner."
       B)   "I imagine" he said, "you will want dinner."
       C)   "I imagine," he said, "you will want dinner."

In numbers 6-10, read the two sentences given and choose whether A or B correctly indicates all the words that should be capitalized.

6.   A)   "Yesterday, grandma Gert came for a visit," said my aunt.
       B)   "Yesterday, grandma Gert came for a visit," said my Aunt.
       C)   "Yesterday, Grandma Gert came for a visit," said my aunt.

7.   A)   The leaves color well in the autumn in the northeast.
       B)   The leaves color well in the Autumn in the Northeast.
       C)   The leaves color well in the autumn in the Northeast.

8.   A)   I heard Governor Bing say that she had majored in Spanish.
       B)   I heard governor Bing say that she had majored in Spanish.
       C)   I heard Governor Bing say that she had majored in spanish.

9.   A)   "The Vietnam War," the woman said, "claimed my son's life."
       B)   "The Vietnam War," the woman said, "Claimed my son's life."
       C)   "The Vietnam war," the woman said, "claimed my son's life."

10.   A)   As far as cookies go, my favorite is the Famous Oreo.
      B)   As far as cookies go, my favorite is the famous Oreo.
      C)   As far as cookies go, my favorite is the famous oreo.

PAYING ATTENTION TO LOOK-ALIKES AND SOUND-ALIKES

Diagnostic Test

Read the two sentences given and choose whether A or B has the correct form of the underlined word(s).

1.   A)   When they're finished, there is coffee they may purchase with their money.
      B)   When their finished, they're is coffee they may purchase with there money.

2.   A)   Who's wearing whose clothes?
      B)   Whose wearing who's cloths?

3.   A)   This is very fine stationery on which she writes.
      B)   This is very fine stationary on which she rights.

4.   A)   With the exception of the chrysanthemums, the whole garden bloomed in June.
      B)   With the accception of the chrysanthemums, the hole garden bloomed in June.

5.   A)   It is a capitol offense to remove anything from the capital building.
      B)   It is a capital offense to remove anything from the capitol building.

6.   A)   Of coarse, babies prefer soft cotton to course wool, weather for close or for bedding.
      B)   Of course, babies prefer soft cotton to coarse wool, whether for clothes or for bedding.

7.   A)   I must compliment you on how well your rugs complement the room.
      B)   I must complement you on how well your rugs compliment the room.

8.   A)   He will go by bus to see his accountant before he will buy the car.
      B)   He will go buy bus to sea his accountant before he will by the car.

9.   A)   The plane truth is that he doesn't like plains.
      B)   The plain truth is that he doesn't like planes.

10.   A)   Its shore hard for Joe to except that everyone is invited accept him.
      B)   It's sure hard for Joe to accept that everyone is invited except him.

Exercise A

Choose the letter (A, B, or C) that is followed by the word that correctly fills the blank.

1.   Mary told her to _____ on the bed for an hour before coming down for dinner.
      A)   lay
      B)   lie
      C)   laid

2.   She pulled down the shades to darken the room, and then she drew the curtains closed _____.
A)   two
B)   too
C)   to

3.   Ann _____ to reflect on her two children to soothe her weary head.
A)   choose
B)   chosen
C)   chose

4.   She took some pillows from a chair near the window, and _____ her aching feet to a slight elevation.
A)   rose
B)   raise
C)   raised

5.   An old brown teddy bear with a plaid vest _____ on the pillow beside her.
A)   sat
B)   sit
C)   sitted

6.   With most of its fur worn quite thin, it appeared to be _____ loved.
A)   special
B)   especially
C)   specially

7.   **While she rested, she thought about the _____ Mary had given her.**
A)   **advise**
B)   **advice**
C)   **advices**

8.   The wise words would prove to greatly _____ the final outcome.
A)   affect
B)   effect
C)   afect

9.   If she wanted to get any _____ with her request, she should rethink her stategy.
A)   farther
B)   further
C)   father

10.   She loosened her _____ for more comfort.
A)   cloths
B)   close
C)   clothes

11.   All _____ the afternoon she tried to convince the committee of her son's needs.

A)   through
B)   threw
C)   though

Harcourt, Inc.

12. They all asked her more medical questions ____ she had anticipated.

    A) than
    B) then
    C) ten

13. The chairman also refused to ____ her request for nursing care.

    A) axcept
    B) except
    C) accept

14. While speaking with Mary over coffee, she agreed with Mary's wise ____ about obtaining physicians' written recommendations.

    A) council
    B) counsel
    C) consel

15. Finally, with the peace and ____ of the early evening, she fell asleep.

    A) quiet
    B) quite
    C) quit

Exercise B

Choose the letter (A, B, or C) that is followed by the word that correctly fills the blank.

1. It is a common ____ with us to take out the horses at sunset.
    A) costume
    B) custom
    C) customer

2. From the meadow, the sight of the setting sun can take your ____ away.
    A) breath
    B) breathe
    C) breathed

3. Except for the three of us, the countryside looks ____.
    A) desert
    B) dessert
    C) deserted

4. We are all ____ of the last remaining days fefore school starts.
    A) conscious
    B) conscience
    C) conscientious

5.   After we came to a higher spot, we ____ on the grass while the horses rested.
        A)   sat
        B)   set
        C)   sit

6.   We talked about how quickly the summer days ____ before us.
        A)   past
        B)   passed
        C)   paste

7.   It was a most activity-filled summer with very little ____.
        A)   reign
        B)   rain
        C)   rein

8.   Back at the camp, the rest of the ____ rested before dinner.
        A)   personnel
        B)   personal
        C)   personality

9.   We, however, couldn't bear to miss the spectacular ____ of a setting sun.
        A)   site
        B)   cite
        C)   sight

10.   "____ view from horseback is always better," the head counselor would say.
        A)   Your
        B)   You're
        C)   Yore

11.   We were quiet on the ride back, as the horses seemed to know ____ way.
        A)   they're
        B)   their
        C)   there

12.   We knew we'd miss all the children ____ lives had touched us that summer.
        A)   whose
        B)   who's
        C)   whoose

13.   We knew they would miss us ____.
        A)   too
        B)   to
        C)   two

14.   Watching children play at summer camp is almost a sure thing at ____ spirits.
        A)   rising
        B)   razing
        C)   raising

                      Harcourt, Inc.

15. Consequently, working as a camp counselor does wonderful things to the ____.
   A)   moral
   B)   morale
   C)   mural

Exercise C

Choose the letter (A, B, or C) that is followed by the word that correctly fills the blank.

1.   Training at competitive sports is very challenging; however, dedicated athletes seldom ____.
   A)   quiet
   B)   quite
   C)   quit

2.   All the effort and hard work often seem to a winner to be her most ____ triumph.
   A)   personal
   B)   personnel
   C)   personality

3.   A focused athlete knows that only ____ dedicated training can she succeed.
   A)   threw
   B)   through
   C)   thorough

4.   Only when she's confident that she put forth her total effort is her ____ clear.
   A)   conscientious
   B)   conscious
   C)   conscience

5.   ____ really a matter of desire, persistence, and concentration.
   A)   Its
   B)   It's
   C)   Its'

6.   Even if she were to ____, just getting the competitive exposure is crucial to a beginning athlete.
   A)   loose
   B)   louse
   C)   lose

7.   For the younger athletes, in just working through the competitive circuit, ____ building early patterns of disciplined competitive behaviors.
   A)   their
   B)   there
   C)   they're

8.   Good sportsmanship is just as important as performing well; responsible athletes learn there is a ____ way to act among fellow competitors.
   A)   rite
   B)   write
   C)   right

9.   For almost any competitor it is painful to _____ defeat.
        A)   accept
        B)   axcept
        C)   except

10.   However, a true winner can _____ to be gracious in times of loss.
        A)   choose
        B)   chosen
        C)   chose

11.   A well-admired runner reveals this to her readers in the _____ of her recent book.
        A)   foreword
        B)   forward
        C)   fourword

12.   A true champion's grace and character _____ her form and speed.
        A)   compliment
        B)   complement
        C)   complimentary

13.   Spectators love when an official _____ the gold medal to an athlete who demonstrates all the true
        virtues of a champion.
        A)   presence
        B)   prezents
        C)   presents

14.   Displaying graceful dignity when a fellow competitor takes the victory is one of the important
        _____ of passage for an athlete.
        A)   rights
        B)   rites
        C)   writes

15.   Participation and competition is _____ the biggest achievement _____.
        A)   we're, lay
        B)   where, lies
        C)   wear, lays

Exercise D

Correct the words that are used incorrectly in the paragraph.

When I was a small child, every Sunday in July and August my grandparents would take my sister

and me too Atlantic City. In those days there we're no casinos, just grand Moorish hotels that

lined the Boardwalk. The Boardwalk was always filled with strolling tourists who's only close

where bathing suits. Benches lined the railings wear those who rested gazed out across the beach to

the see. Of coarse, there were the grand amusement piers that stretched out from the Boardwalk. At night, when the tide was high, the water would come up write under the Boardwalk. You could

look out over the rail and sea the see below, with moonlight reflecting off the waves.

Exercise E

Correct the words that are used incorrectly in the paragraph.

Probably the most famous of these grand amusement piers was the Steel Pier. As well as carousels

and other amusements, their where various shows and animal acts on the pier. At night, the place

was quiet a spectacle. Their where many exciting things to see they're. However, the one thing

that stands out vividly in my memory is the famous Diving Horse Show. A beautiful girl would

ride a horse up a ramp to a platform high above a large pool of water. After they we're at the top,

too the crowd's amazement, horse and diver would dive rite off the platform and plunge into the

water below. Than the hole crowd would applaud wildly with the big splash.

Exercise F

Correct the words that are used incorrectly in the paragraph.

In the midst of all that cheering, however, I always felt quiet sad. I wondered if given a choose, the

horse would chose to do something that seemed too me so unnatural for a horse two do. But alas,

going to the Diving Horse Show was a summer costume to most people who vacationed at the

New Jersey seashore. I just couldn't stop thinking about that horse when the show was over. I'd do

the same thing each time -- walk back out on the Boardwalk passed the salt-water taffy stand,

clutch my grandfather's hand, breath in the salt air, and shiver at the thought of it all. Its a

memory I'll always carry with me.

Mastery Test

Read the two sentences given and choose whether A or B has the correct forms of the underlined words.

1. A) Its the chose of the personal weather or not employees where uniforms.
    B) It's the choice of the personnel whether or not employees wear uniforms.

2. A) All patients will be seen by the residents at the office today.
    B) All patience will be scene by the residence at the office today.

3. A) Of coarse, its a matter of personnel opinion witch close are most suitable.
    B) Of course, it's a matter of personal opinion which clothes are most suitable.

4. A) He is quite sure the investigation of the crash site was thorough.
    B) He is quiet sure the investigation of the crash cite was through.

5. A) Except for the adopted cat, whose meows were heard from the garage, all the presents were opened.
    B) Accept for the adapted cat, who's meows where herd from the garage, all the presence were opened.

6. **A)** I must complement you on the most dignified way you're dog sets waiting for his meal.
    B) I must compliment you on the most dignified way your dog sits waiting for his meal.

7. **A)** In her recommendation letter, written on ivory stationery, she cites many examples of her student's abilities.
    B) In her recommendation letter, written on ivory stationary, she sights many examples of her student's abilities.

8. A) Through the whole race her voice grew hoarse cheering for the runner with the graceful gait.
    B) Threw the whole race her voice grew horse cheering for the runner with the graceful gate.

9. A) With a short break in the conversation the quiet boy ate his dessert.
    B) With a short brake in the conversation the quite boy ate his desert.

10. A) I shall look forward to the day I write the foreward to the book.
    B) I shall look foreward to the day I write the forward to the book.

Harcourt, Inc.

IRREGULAR VERBS

Diagnostic Test

Each sentence contains a blank. Choose the letter (A, B, or C) that is followed by the form of the irregular verb that correctly completes the sentence.

1.   After we had _____ much raking, the leaves were all in large piles around the yard.
        A)   do
        B)   done
        C)   did

2.   "Always be careful of what _____ within leaf piles," my parents always told me.
        A)   lain
        B)   lays
        C)   lies

3.   Once again they _____ me this advice as my son jumps in the biggest pile.
        A)   give
        B)   gave
        C)   given

4.   Once my uncle, it was often told, _____ a spider that was quite dangerous.
        A)   catch
        B)   catched
        C)   caught

5.   I paid no mind as I _____ among the biggest piles.
        A)   sat
        B)   sit
        C)   set

6.   My brother, who has quite a creative imagination, can _____ some wild tales.
        A)   wove
        B)   weave
        C)   woven

7.   He once told us he had been _____ in a snow bank for an hour before he was found.
        A)   frozen
        B)   froze
        C)   freeze

8.   Then he said that he could _____ sounds that were extremely high in pitch.
        A)   hear
        B)   heard
        C)   heared

9.   I always thought my mother must have dropped him when she _____ him home from the hospital.
        A)   brung
        B)   bring
        C)   brought

10. Yet, friends and family have _____ for hours listening to his crazy exploits.
    A)   sat
    B)   sit
    C)   sitted

Exercise A

Choose the letter (A, B, or C) of the sentence in which the underlined irregular verb is used correctly.

1.   A)   With January's storm, the iced branches of the birch had <u>bent</u> nearly to the ground.
      B)   With January's storm, the iced branches of the birch had <u>bended</u> nearly to the ground.
      C)   With January's storm, the iced branches of the birch had <u>bend</u> nearly to the ground

2.   A)   Moments after the clock struck midnight, the boy <u>creep</u> downstairs as quietly as he could.
      B)   Moments after the clock struck midnight, the boy <u>creeped</u> downstairs as quietly as he could.
      C)   Moments after the clock struck midnight, the boy <u>crept</u> downstairs as quietly as he could.

3.   A)   In no time at all he <u>won</u> them over with his sweetness.
      B)   In no time at all he <u>winned</u> them over with his sweetness.
      C)   In no time at all he <u>win</u> them over with his sweetness.

4.   A)   He <u>wrung</u> out the sweater despite the instructions on the label.
      B)   He <u>wring</u> out the sweater despite the instructions on the label.
      C)   He <u>rung</u> out the sweater despite the instructions on the label.

5.   A)   The counselor asked them, "How much warm clothing have you <u>brung</u>?"
      B)   The counselor asked them, "How much warm clothing have you <u>bring</u>?"
      C)   The counselor asked them, "How much warm clothing have you <u>brought</u>?"

6.   A)   Singing softly to herself, the girl <u>dug</u> all afternoon in the warm white sand.
      B)   Singing softly to herself, the girl <u>digged</u> all afternoon in the warm white sand.
      C)   Singing softly to herself, the girl <u>dig</u> all afternoon in the warm white sand.

7.   A)   He <u>feel</u> a keen sense of hunger all afternoon that interfered with his concentration.
      B)   He <u>felt</u> a keen sense of hunger all afternoon that interfered with his concentration.
      C)   He <u>feeled</u> a keen sense of hunger all afternoon that interfered with his concentration.

8.   A)   I have <u>bet</u> him that the team will make the finals this year.
      B)   I have <u>beat</u> him that the team will make the finals this year.
      C)   I have <u>betted</u> him that the team will make the finals this year.

9.   A)   She really hopes her grandmother's beautifully ornate wedding dress will <u>fit</u> her.
      B)   She really hopes her grandmother's beautifully ornate wedding dress will <u>fitted</u> her.
      C)   She really hopes her grandmother's beautifully ornate wedding dress will <u>fat</u> her.

10.   A)   The date has been <u>setted</u>; he will begin his cross-country trip on June 18.
      B)   The date has been <u>sat</u>; he will begin his cross-country trip on June 18.
      C)   The date has been <u>set</u>; he will begin his cross-country trip on June 18.

11. A) Jane has <u>becomed</u> quite excited about the pediatric residency in nephrology.
    B) Jane has <u>became</u> quite excited about the pediatric residency in nephrology.
    C) Jane has <u>become</u> quite excited about the pediatric residency in nephrology.

12. A) He went last month to the concert in Pigeon Forge; his brother Al <u>goed</u> with him.
    B) He went last month to the concert in Pigeon Forge; his brother Al <u>gone</u> with him.
    C) He went last month to the concert in Pigeon Forge; his brother Al <u>went</u> with him.

13. A) She went to the anti-vivisection demonstration, even though her mother strictly <u>forbade</u> her.
    B) She went to the anti-vivisection demonstration, even though her mother strictly <u>forbid</u> her.
    C) She went to the anti-vivisection demonstration, even though her mother strictly <u>forbidden</u> her.

14. A) Has she <u>get</u> all her letters of recommendation for her graduate school application?
    B) Has she <u>got</u> all her letters of recommendation for her graduate school application?
    C) Has she <u>gotten</u> all her letters of recommendation for her graduate school application?

15. A) They walked all the way, and an icy February wind <u>blowed</u> from the north.
    B) They walked all the way, and an icy February wind <u>blew</u> from the north.
    C) They walked all the way, and an icy February wind <u>blown</u> from the north.

Exercise B

Choose the letter (A, B, or C) of th sentence in which the underlined irregular verb is used correctly.

1. A) When the child smiled up at me, I knew he had <u>broken</u> the plate.
    B) When the child smiled up at me, I knew he had <u>broke</u> the plate.
    C) When the child smiled up at me, I knew he had <u>break</u> the plate.

2. A) For dinner she has <u>chosen</u> a Mandarin chicken dish with rice and vegetables.
    B) For dinner she has <u>chose</u> a Mandarin chicken dish with rice and vegetables.
    C) For dinner she has <u>choose</u> a Mandarin chicken dish with rice and vegetables.

3. A) As he told the story, his mother <u>began</u> to bubble with laughter.
    B) As he told the story, his mother <u>begun</u> to bubble with laughter.
    C) As he told the story, his mother <u>begin</u> to bubble with laughter.

4. A) The player <u>throw</u> the ball to second after he caught the fly ball.
    B) The player <u>threw</u> the ball to second after he caught the fly ball.
    C) The player <u>thrown</u> the ball to second after he caught the fly ball.

5   A) After the child <u>drank</u> all his milk, he began to doze off in her arms.
    B) After the child <u>drink</u> all his milk, he began to doze off in her arms.
    C) After the child <u>drunk</u> all his milk, he began to doze off in her arms.

6. A) After a scrumptious dinner, it was revealed that he had <u>stole</u> the recipe from the innkeeper's desk when we stayed last year.
   B) After a scrumptious dinner, it was revealed that he had <u>stolen</u> the recipe from the innkeeper's desk when we stayed last year.
   C) After a scrumptious dinner, it was revealed that he had <u>stealed</u> the recipe from the innkeeper's desk when we stayed last year.

7. A) Has young Harold <u>put</u> on his winter coat, scarf, and gloves?
   B) Has young Harold <u>putted</u> on his winter coat, scarf, and gloves?
   C) Has young Harold <u>pet</u> on his winter coat, scarf, and gloves?

8. A) The baseball card, if it was in good condition, must have <u>cost</u> a great deal.
   B) The baseball card, if it was in good condition, must have <u>cast</u> a great deal.
   C) The baseball card, if it was in good condition, must have <u>costed</u> a great deal.

9. A) Before she left, she <u>mean</u> to set the VCR to record the Civil War documentary.
   B) Before she left, she <u>mint</u> to set the VCR to record the Civil War documentary.
   C) Before she left, she <u>meant</u> to set the VCR to record the Civil War documentary.

10. A) The agitated visitor tossed, turned, and hardly <u>sleeped</u> a wink.
    B) The agitated visitor tossed, turned, and hardly <u>sleep</u> a wink.
    C) The agitated visitor tossed, turned, and hardly <u>slept</u> a wink.

11. A) Deep in the woods is the fort the brothers had <u>build</u> as children.
    B) Deep in the woods is the fort the brothers had <u>built</u> as children.
    C) Deep in the woods is the fort the brothers had <u>builded</u> as children.

12. A) I've <u>spoken</u> to him about the class trip; I will chaperone this year.
    B) I've <u>spoke</u> to him about the class trip; I will chaperone this year.
    C) I've <u>speak</u> to him about the class trip; I will chaperone this year.

13. A) Last September he had <u>taken</u> her back to Provence, where she was born.
    B) Last September he had <u>taked</u> her back to Provence, where she was born.
    C) Last September he had <u>took</u> her back to Provence, where she was born.

14. A) The gentlemen <u>strode</u> through the office in their elegant suits before the awards dinner.
    B) The gentlemen <u>stride</u> through the office in their elegant suits before the awards dinner.
    C) The gentlemen <u>stridden</u> through the office in their elegant suits before the awards dinner.

15. A) That young journalist has <u>written</u> an especially sensitive account of the tragedy.
    B) That young journalist has <u>write</u> an especially sensitive account of the tragedy.
    C) That young journalist has <u>wrote</u> an especially sensitive account of the tragedy.

Exercise C

Choose the letter (A, B, or C) of the sentence in which the underlined irregular verb is used correctly.

1. A) She answered the door, and he told her that he <u>tear</u> his suit jacket when he fell.
   B) She answered the door, and he told her that he <u>tore</u> his suit jacket when he fell.
   C) She answered the door, and he told her that he <u>torn</u> his suit jacket when he fell.

Harcourt, Inc.

2. A) Whenever that demon of mediocrity tells you to <u>quit</u>, breathe deep and press on.
    B) Whenever that demon of mediocrity tells you to <u>quite</u>, breathe deep and press on.
    C) Whenever that demon of mediocrity tells you to <u>quitted</u>, breathe deep and press on.

3. A) The old brown horse <u>stridden</u> happily through the green pasture.
    B) The old brown horse <u>stride</u> happily through the green pasture.
    C) The old brown horse <u>strode</u> happily through the green pasture.

4. A) Diane <u>send</u> me a leopard costume that her son had from elementary school.
    B) Diane <u>sent</u> me a leopard costume that her son had from elementary school.
    C) Diane <u>scent</u> me a leopard costume that her son had from elementary school.

5. A) Someone was very mysterious to have <u>begun</u> planting flowers in my yard.
    B) Someone was very mysterious to have <u>begin</u> planting flowers in my yard.
    C) Someone was very mysterious to have <u>began</u> planting flowers in my yard.

6. A) Have you ever had the pleasure to <u>met</u> our wonderful plumber, Ernie?
    B) Have you ever had the pleasure to <u>meet</u> our wonderful plumber, Ernie?
    C) Have you ever had the pleasure to <u>meat</u> our wonderful plumber, Ernie?

7. A) She wants to use ivory satin to <u>bound</u> the edges of his blanket.
    B) She wants to use ivory satin to <u>bind</u> the edges of his blanket.
    C) She wants to use ivory satin to <u>bend</u> the edges of his blanket.

8. A) I <u>new</u> I made the right decision when I looked into her kind eyes.
    B) I <u>knew</u> I made the right decision when I looked into her kind eyes.
    C) I <u>known</u> I made the right decision when I looked into her kind eyes.

9. A) "Can you tell me who was there when the doorbell <u>ring</u> at 7:00?"
    B) "Can you tell me who was there when the doorbell <u>rung</u> at 7:00?"
    C) "Can you tell me who was there when the doorbell <u>rang</u> at 7:00?"

10. A) Has that woman <u>sang</u> here every Christmas eve service?
    B) Has that woman <u>sing</u> here every Christmas eve service?
    C) Has that woman <u>sung</u> here every Christmas eve service?

11. A) That naughty boy released the bird that <u>flew</u> all around the house.
    B) That naughty boy released the bird that <u>fly</u> all around the house.
    C) That naughty boy released the bird that <u>flown</u> all around the house.

12. A) Mrs. Kane has <u>grow</u> beautiful purple irises ever since she moved here.
    B) Mrs. Kane has <u>grew</u> beautiful purple irises ever since she moved here.
    C) Mrs. Kane has <u>grown</u> beautiful purple irises ever since she moved here.

13. A) Were you angry last Wednesday night that her dog had <u>bit</u> your dog?
    B) Were you angry last Wednesday night that her dog had <u>bite</u> your dog?
    C) Were you angry last Wednesday night that her dog had <u>bitten</u> your dog?

14.   A)   She had always <u>knew</u> he would succeed in anything he did with passion.
            B)   She had always <u>known</u> he would succeed in anything he did with passion.
            C)   She had always <u>know</u> he would succeed in anything he did with passion.

15.   A)   Aunt Em's recipes are in the left drawer; I have <u>keep</u> this secret for years.
            B)   Aunt Em's recipes are in the left drawer; I have <u>keeped</u> this secret for years.
            C)   Aunt Em's recipes are in the left drawer; I have <u>kept</u> this secret for years.

Exercise D

Choose the letter (A, B, or C) of the sentence in which the underlined irregular verbs are used correctly.

1.   A)   She has <u>became</u> a very good friend to me over the years we have <u>knew</u> each other.
            B)   She has <u>become</u> a very good friend to me over the years we have <u>known</u> each other.
            C)   She has <u>became</u> a very good friend to me over the years we have <u>known</u> each other.

2.   A)   The man <u>shaken</u> hands with the boy, after he had <u>ran</u> down the hall to give him the news.
            B)   The man <u>shook</u> hands with the boy, after he had <u>run</u> down the hall to give him the news.
            C)   The man <u>shook</u> hands with the boy, after he had <u>ran</u> to give him the news.

3.   A)   After she had <u>ridden</u> the whole way, she felt a sense of accomplishment, having <u>known</u> there was a bus that went there everyday.
            B)   After she had <u>rode</u> the whole way, she felt a sense of accomplishment, having <u>known</u> there was a bus that went there everyday.
            C)   After she had <u>ride</u> the whole way, she felt a sense of accomplishment, having <u>know</u> there was a bus that went there everyday.

4.   A)   She <u>knowed</u> the cut was going to <u>bled</u> heavily, because it occurred in a very vascular area.
            B)   She <u>knew</u> the cut was going to <u>bleed</u> heavily, because it occurred in a very vascular area.
            C)   She <u>know</u> the cut was going to <u>bleed</u> heavily, because it occurred in a very vascular area.

5.   A)   She never <u>quit</u> arguing with me about the fact that my son had <u>swum</u> in her pool when the family was vacationing in San Antonio.
            B)   She never <u>quitted</u> arguing with me about the fact that my son had <u>swim</u> in her pool when the family was vacationing in San Antonio.
            C)   She never <u>quit</u> arguing with me about the fact that my son had <u>swam</u> in her pool when the family was vacationing in San Antonio.

6.   A)   I <u>drove</u> all the way to Kingston and <u>bought</u> a blue vest for my son's school photographs.
            B)   I <u>drive</u> all the way to Kingston and <u>bought</u> a blue vest for my son's school photographs.
            C)   I <u>drove</u> all the way to Kingston and <u>buy</u> a blue vest for my son's school photographs.

7.   A)   I never <u>know</u> that last semester she had <u>written</u> her entire draft of her essay on Austen's *Sense and Sensibility*.
            B)   I never <u>knew</u> that last semester she had <u>written</u> her entire draft of her essay on Austen's *Sense and Sensibility*.
            C)   I never <u>knew</u> that last semester she had <u>wrote</u> her entire draft of her essay on Austen's *Sense and Sensibility*.

                       Harcourt, Inc.

8. A) Yesterday, after the difficult seminar the night before, she <u>rised</u> at noon and <u>swam</u> in the lake to relax and unwind.
    B) Yesterday, after the difficult seminar the night before, she <u>rose</u> at noon and <u>swum</u> in the lake to relax and unwind.
    C) Yesterday, after the difficult seminar the night before, she <u>rose</u> at noon and <u>swam</u> in the lake to relax and unwind.

9. A) The icy cold wind had <u>blown</u> from the north all day, after the storm <u>hit</u> the night before.
    B) The icy cold wind had <u>blew</u> from the north all day, after the storm <u>hit</u> the night before.
    C) The icy cold wind had <u>blow</u> from the north all day, after the storm <u>hit</u> the night before.

10. A) When I saw him last week, I was amazed at how much he had <u>grown</u>; the coat I <u>bought</u> would never fit him.
    B) When I saw him last week, I was amazed at how much he had <u>grew</u>; the coat I <u>bought</u> would never fit him.
    C) When I saw him last week, I was amazed at how much he had <u>grown</u>; the coat I <u>buy</u> would never fit him.

11. A) She <u>wept</u> when she learned that her mother had <u>threw</u> away her journals from college.
    B) She <u>wept</u> when she learned that her mother had <u>thrown</u> away her journals from college.
    C) She <u>weeped</u> when she learned that her mother had <u>thrown</u> away her journals from college.

12. A) We saw she had <u>drunk</u> all her milk, and we watched as she <u>slept</u> through the next hour.
    B) We saw she had <u>drank</u> all her milk, and we watched as she <u>slept</u> through the next hour.
    C) We saw she had <u>drunk</u> all her milk, and we watched as she <u>sleeps</u> through the next hour.

13. A) She <u>sought</u> for the bike the entire summer before she discovered he had <u>hidden</u> it in the bushes so it wouldn't be <u>stole</u>.
    B) She <u>sought</u> for the bike the entire summer before she discovered he had <u>hidden</u> it in the bushes so it wouldn't be <u>stolen</u>.
    C) She <u>sook</u> for the bike the entire summer before she discovered he had <u>hidden</u> it in the bushes so it wouldn't be <u>stealed</u>.

14. A) She had <u>swum</u> in the lake every summer as a girl; her father <u>taught</u> her to swim the very first week he <u>brought</u> her to the beach.
    B) She had <u>swam</u> in the lake every summer as a girl; her father <u>taught</u> her to swim the very first week he <u>brought</u> her to the beach.
    C) She had <u>swum</u> in the lake every summer as a girl; her father <u>teach</u> her to swim the very first week he <u>brought</u> her to the beach.

15. A) She <u>spent</u> all afternoon listening as the telephone <u>rang</u> again and again; she wouldn't answer, so the caller <u>kept</u> calling.
    B) She <u>spent</u> all afternoon listening as the telephone <u>rung</u> again and again; she wouldn't answer, so the caller <u>kept</u> calling.
    C) She <u>spent</u> all afternoon listening as the telephone <u>rang</u> again and again; she wouldn't answer, so the caller <u>keep</u> calling.

Exercise E

Edit and change the verbs that are not in the correct form.

There in the middle of the forest standed a rustic cabin. As we walked through the door, all at once the smell of cedar bringed back so many memories of my childhood summers at the lake. One would almost think with all the years that I would have forgot how much I loved those timesùthe hikes through the woods, the fire crackling as we eated fresh trout we catched that afternoon. But I recall nights watching the fireflies dot the darkness across the lake, believing I had never saw a sight so peaceful. Now I look up through the cabin window to the clarity of the stars in the blackest sky I have ever saw, and I know with all certainty I have not losed sight of things past nor forgetted their beauty.

Exercise F

Edit and change the verbs that are not in the correct form.

Dear Carmella,

When the guests arrive, I do not believe they will have ate. I spoke to them at noon when they stopped for lunch. They said they were driving non-stop the rest of the way. After their long drive, they will probably have grew quite hungry and tired. They will have rode all day without stopping for dinner. It would be nice to leave a tray of assorted grapes, cheeses, crackers, and meats in their room. Leave a chilled bottle of Chardonnay. After they have got a chance to relax a bit, go in with the basket of menus from the restaurants in town. Let them go to dinner. While they're gone, it would be nice to go in and turn down the sheets and leave a tray of chocolates and some of our vintage port. Tomorrow, after they have slept, they will be ready for our tour. The road along the coast should offer them sights they have never saw. I will be back late in the afternoon and will greet them then. Thanks so much for covering for me.

Harcourt, Inc.

Each sentence contains blanks. Choose the letter (A, B, or C) that is followed by the forms of the irregular verbs that correctly complete the sentence.

1.   There, in the driving rain, _____ Randy with no umbrella or coat, as the bus ____ by without stopping.
    A)   stand, rided
    B)   stood, rode
    C)   standed, ridden

2.   Joshua said he had _____ the bell again and again before he finally had ____ the hint they were angry with him over the incident.
    A)   rung, gotten
    B)   rang, gotten
    C)   ring, got

3.   She is from the East Coast and has never _____ in the Pacific; it is an opportunity she will be glad she had ____.
    A)   swum, taken
    B)   swim, took
    C)   swam, taken

4.   The temperature had ____ considerably and still they ____ in the bright sun in bitter protest.
    A)   rise, stand
    B)   risen, stood
    C)   rose, stood

5.   She waited for two hours and then realized he had _____ about their interview, which ____ scheduled for noon.
    A)   forget, been
    B)   forgotten, had been
    C)   forgot, had been

6.   Come promptly at seven; we shall _____ at eight, once all the awards ____ presented.
    A)   eaten, are
    B)   eat, have been
    C)   ate, having been

7.   He performed with ease because he _____ been well trained and had ____ much competition.
    A)   had, seen
    B)   have, seen
    C)   head, saw

8.   They have ____ the beautiful redwoods after they ____ the main sights in the city.
    A)   seen, saw
    B)   saw, seen
    C)   see, seed

9.   After having ____ several hours in the rain, the bicyclists finally ____ the sun.
    A)   rid, saw
    B)   rode, had seen
    C)   ridden, saw

Each sentence contains blanks. Choose the letter (A, B, or C) that is followed by the forms of the irregular verbs that correctly complete the sentence.

1.   There, in the driving rain, _____ Randy with no umbrella or coat, as the bus ____ by without stopping.
   A)   stand, rided
   B)   stood, rode
   C)   standed, ridden

2.   Joshua said he had _____ the bell again and again before he finally had ____ the hint they were angry with him over the incident.
   A)   rung, gotten
   B)   rang, gotten
   C)   ring, got

3.   She is from the East Coast and has never _____ in the Pacific; it is an opportunity she will be glad she had ____.
   A)   swum, taken
   B)   swim, took
   C)   swam, taken

4.   The temperature had ____ considerably and still they ____ in the bright sun in bitter protest.
   A)   rise, stand
   B)   risen, stood
   C)   rose, stood

5.   She waited for two hours and then realized he had _____ about their interview, which ____ scheduled for noon.
   A)   forget, been
   B)   forgotten, had been
   C)   forgot, had been

6.   Come promptly at seven; we shall _____ at eight, once all the awards ____ presented.
   A)   eaten, are
   B)   eat, have been
   C)   ate, having been

7.   He performed with ease because he _____ been well trained and had ____ much competition.
   A)   had, seen
   B)   have, seen
   C)   head, saw

8.   They have ____ the beautiful redwoods after they ____ the main sights in the city.
   A)   seen, saw
   B)   saw, seen
   C)   see, seed

9.   After having ____ several hours in the rain, the bicyclists finally ____ the sun.
   A)   rid, saw
   B)   rode, had seen
   C)   ridden, saw

10. Until this meal, I have not _____ much attention to the joy on the chef's face after the diners ____.
   A)   paid, have eaten
   B)   pay, ate
   C)   payed, ate

ANSWERS

FINDING SUBJECTS AND VERBS IN SIMPLE SENTENCES_(1)

Diagnostic Test_(1)

1. C
2. B
3. A
4. C
5. C
6. B
7. B
8. B
9. C
10. A

Exercise A_(2)

1. cheetah
2. speed
3. legs
4. shoulder blades
5. nostrils and airway
6. lungs
7. claws
8. claws
9. feature
10. pad

Exercise B_(3)

1. B
2. C
3. C
4. C
5. A
6. A
7. C
8. B
9. A
10. C
11. B
12. B
13. C
14. B
15. A

Exercise C_(4)

1.   B
2.   B
3.   B
4.   B
5.   C
6.   C
7.   B
8.   A
9.   A
10.   B
11.   C
12.   B
13.   A
14.   C
15.   C

Exercise D_(6)

The most common type of giraffe is the reticulated giraffe. Its colors have a clear pattern of white lines surrounding the darker brown spots. With their speed, adult animals are relatively safe from predators. Additionally, the giraffe's large hooves also help in its defense. A kick from an adult giraffe can be deadly for predators as fierce as lions. However, while the giraffe drinks, the animal must lower its head down to the water. This makes the giraffe spread its long legs to lower itself. In this position, the giraffe is vulnerable to attack because it takes a long time to stand upright again.

Exercise E_(6)

Elephants are the only non-extinct members of the order *Proboscidea*, in the family *Elephantidae*. Within this family there are two species: the African elephant and the Asian elephant.

African elephants and Asian elephants differ in various ways. The most striking and well-recognized difference is in the ears of the large animals. The Africans' ears are much larger and appear to be shaped much like the continent of Africa. On the other hand, the Asians' ears are smaller. Most often, only male Asian elephants have large tusks. Conversely, both male and female African elephants have large external tusks. African elephants are typically larger, with concave backs and less hairy bodies than their Asian cousins. Most often smaller, the Asian elephants can also be recognized by the bulges on their foreheads and several patches of depigmentation on their bodies.

Harcourt, Inc.

Exercise F_(7)

Aside from their beauty, the zebra's <u>stripes</u> <u>have</u> important functions. Originally, <u>it</u> <u>was believed</u> that the stripes helped the zebras to stay hidden in the shadows behind trees and bushes. Their alternating black and white <u>patterns</u> <u>would resemble</u> the filtered light of the sun shining down through branches. Actually, <u>zebras</u> <u>are</u> often <u>seen</u> in open areas. This <u>fact</u>, then, <u>would seem to dispute</u> this camouflage theory.

Others believe the <u>stripes</u> <u>act</u> as a distraction to predators who become confused as the sight of a zebra herd. Focusing on a single animal, a <u>lion</u> <u>sees</u> a blur of black and white as the herd scrambles. Still other <u>theories</u> <u>support</u> the fact that the <u>stripes</u>, as distinctive as fingerprints, <u>serve</u> as aids in recognition. After <u>zebras</u>, often living in mixed herds of antelope and gnus, <u>flee</u> from predators, their <u>stripes</u> <u>can help</u> them find each other again.

Mastery Test_(8)

1. B
2. B
3. A
4. C
5 A
6. B
7. C
8. C
9. C
10. A

MAKING SUBJECTS AND VERBS AGREE_(9)

Diagnostic Test_(9)

1. A
2. A
3. A
4. A
5. B
6. B
7. B
8. B
9. B
10. A

Exercise A_(10)

1. A
2. B
3. B
4. B
5. B

6. B
7. A
8. A
9. A
10. B
11. B
12. B
13. A
14. A
15. B

Exercise B_(11)

1. B
2. A
3. A
4. A
5. B
6. A
7. B
8. B
9. B
10. B
11. **A**
12. **A**
13. **B**
14. **A**
15. **B**

Exercise C_(12)

1. B
2. A
3. B
4. A
5. A
6. B
7. A
8. B
9. B
10. A
11. B
12. A
13. A
14. A
15. B

Exercise D_(13)

In the safety of the school nurse's office is the familiarity of bandages, sterile cotton, and antiseptic. Mrs. Gaines touches his shoulder, telling him with the reassurance of the pressure: everything is going to be all right. In that fact, he surrenders and lets her clean his scraped and bloody forearm. It really stings, he thinks to himself, but not with the same burning of physical pain. In the moment before he <u>falls</u>, the ball soaring over his head, he <u>knows</u>. The bigger boys, in all the excitement of their game, <u>see</u> him as merely Tom's little brother. Everyone <u>knows</u> he won't catch passes like that. What they don't <u>know</u> is how like salt their laughter <u>adds</u> to the sting of the wound.

Exercise E_(14)

From his window, he <u>sees</u> that snow has fallen, just as the radio voice had promised. Everywhere -- rooftops, fields, bare tree branches -- snow <u>glistens</u> in the clear sunlight. Then, as it will on every snow-filled weekday morning of his hope-filled boyhood, his heart <u>leaps</u>. What <u>lies</u> on the other side of the window <u>are</u> hours without the geometry of triangles in math class. There <u>is</u> just white without bells to ring in the next 42-minute class period.

"There <u>is </u>nothing to make a fuss over," Dad calls from the kitchen. But Dad <u>doesn't</u> know this feeling – or at least <u>doesn't</u> remember. In the days before worry over lost wages or having enough seasoned wood, there <u>is</u> every reason for wonder over this otherwise ordinary Thursday. For a boy of six, something <u>feels</u> extraordinary about letting himself fall backward into the accumulated inches, waving his arms and legs to leave an angelic mark in the fresh snow.

Exercise F_(14)

Crossing the back lot, walking through the tangle of dead leaves and brush, I <u>see</u> what <u>makes</u> most people <u>reflect</u> on warm summer afternoons. In the cold air, Mr. Kane's white shirts <u>flip</u> on the line tied from pole to pole. All the trees, except for the holly, <u>are</u> bare, so the flapping shirts <u>make</u> quite a racket in the wind.

Something about the scene -- with the crisp sound of the cotton -- <u>warms</u> me inside, just thinking of all of Mrs. Kane's efforts at scrubbing collars and cuffs, Most of the residents along the lake <u>head</u> for warmer places for these colder months. Yet, somehow seeing all those shirts <u>makes</u> it feel like the grand circus of an August afternoon.

Mastery Test_(15)

1. A
2. A
3. B
4. A
5. B
6. A
7. A
8. A
9. B
10. A

CORRECTING THE FRAGMENT IN SIMPLE SENTENCES_(16)

Diagnostic Test_(16)

1. B
2. C

3.   A
4.   D
5.   D
6.   B or C
7.   A
8.   D
9.   B or C
10.   C

Exercise A_(17)

1.   B
2.   A
3.   A
4.   D
5.   C
6.   B or C
7.   B or C
8.   A
9.   A
10.   D
11.   B
12.   C
13.   C
14.   A
15.   A

Exercise B_(17)

1.   A
2.   B
3.   D
4.   C
5.   B or C
6.   C
7.   A
8.   C
9.   D
10.   D
11.   B
12.   A
13.   A
14.   D
15.   C

Exercise C_(18)

1.   D
2.   D
3.   D
4.   A
5.   B
6.   B

7. D
8. A
9. D
10. D
11. A
12. C
13. A
14. B or C
15. D

Exercise D_(19)

Answers may vary. This is one possible answer.

In America's temperate zones, autumn's cooler nights and shortened hours of daylight, <u>bring</u> the finale to the long warm days of summer. Because weather <u>can vary</u> this time of year, only the most favorable conditions contribute to the most intensely-colored foliage displays. Ideally, nights are cool, but not reaching down into freezing temperatures<u>, which</u> only causes leaves to wither, turn brown, and fall. But, when weather cooperates, rich golds, bold reds, and even magestic purples <u>can color</u> the canopy of leaves over a path through the woods in the Northeast. Meanwhile, on the farther coast, <u>westerners</u> enjoy the bronzing of tall oaks on the Livermore Hills east of San Francisco.

Exercise E_(19)

Answers may vary. This is one possible answer.

Understanding the very basic science of leaf <u>coloration can</u> make observation more interesting. The gradual, but quite dazzling, color changes among the leaves of deciduous trees like oaks, hickories, sumacs, maples, aspens, and <u>gums occur</u> only in America's temperate zones. And, among these areas, the display in the East <u>is</u> especially brilliant in its colors of autumn foliage. Exceptionally breathtaking views can be seen by travelers on New England roadway tours<u>, known</u> for the sugar maples ablaze in fiery red. This incredible backdrop of color <u>has</u> awed vacationers for countless autumn seasons.

Exercise F_(20)

Rewrite the following paragraphs, correcting all fragment errors.

<u>Inside the cell tissue of leaves are tiny capsules</u> of green pigment called chlorophyll.. During the warm summer <u>months, chlorophyll</u> participates in food and energy processes in the leaves. Inside the capsules of chlorophyll <u>are two</u> other pigments called carotenoids. However, xanthophyll (which is yellow) and carotene (which is orange) are masked during the summer months by the working chlorophyll.

By summer's end, with the decrease in sunlight hours and the temperatures at <u>night, the</u> leaves' living processes begin to slow down. Chlorophyll undergoes a rapid deterioration, eventually disappearing. Only the xanthophyll and carotene are left, and the leaves begin their color transformation to yellows and oranges.

Exercise G_(20)

Answers may vary. This is one possible answer.

There is another group of color pigments responsible for perhaps the most dramatic <u>coloration,</u> <u>though</u> not as commonly occurring in leaves as carotenoids. These pigments are <u>anthocyanins,</u> <u>which,</u> unlike carotenoids, are not present in the summer months. Also unlike carotenoids, these pigments not confined inside the capsules of chlorophyll. Instead, anthocyanins are first formed in autumn and appear in the uppermost cell layers<u>. Anthocyanins</u> dominate over other pigments present deeper. The pigments can variously <u>combine to bring</u> reds and magentas and blues and purples to leaves.

Leaves containing anthocyanins can offer the must unusual colors and variations. Their combination with carotenoids in different layers of the leaves <u>can bring</u> out the most extraordinary colors. Even leaves on the same tree can appear to have subtle differences in <u>color because</u> of slight combinations of their pigments.

Mastery Test_(21)

1. C
2. D
3. A
4. C
5. B or C
6. B or C
7. A
8. D
9. A
10. C

COMBINING SENTENCES USING THE THREE METHODS OF COORDINATION_(51)

Diagnostic Test_(21)

1. B
2. B
3. A
4. C
5. B
6. C
7. B
8. C
9. A
10. B

Exercise A_(23)

1. C
2. C

3. A
4. B
5. A
6. B
7. C
8. B
9. A
10. B
11. B
12. C
13. B
14. A
15. A

Exercise B_(25)

1. A
2. B
3. B
4. C
5. A
6. C
7. A
8. C
9. B
10. A
11. C
12. C
13. A
14. A
15. A

Exercise C_(26)

1. A
2. B
3. A
4. C
5. A
6. B
7. B
8. A
9. B
10. A
11. A
12. C
13. B
14. A
15. B

Exercise D_(28)

1. B

2.   A
3.   C
4.   A
5.   A
6.   B
7.   C
8.   B
9.   A
10.   A
11.   B
12.   C
13.   A
14.   B
15.   B

Exercise E_(30)

Answers may vary. This is one possible answer.

Many Americans are becoming more health conscious. Some of these same people are demanding foods free of chemicals, and they also desire living in a cleaner and safer environment. As a result of some of these concerns, organic gardening has become popular in recent years. Gardening organically involves a closer connection between the gardener and nature. This method doesn't have to be difficult, for it centers on only two basic principles. First, the organic gardener recycles natural materials. This maintains the soil's fertility. Then, rather than using chemicals, pest and disease control is achieved with natural methods. These basic principles mirror those found in nature, so applying these in the organic garden will yield fruits and vegetables that are not only delicious but also healthy, and chemical-free.

Exercise F_(30)

Answers may vary. This is one possible answer.

Chicken tenders are the smaller thin strips of meat that come from either side of the breast bone. These pieces are smaller than the breast; in fact, both pieces can weigh less than one-half of the chicken breast. Some people prefer these strips; indeed, their tenderness makes them delicious in saut_ed dishes. Using tenders rather than the breast can allow for shorter cooking times because of the strips' size and tenderness; thus, this can be most convenient when time is short. Cooking with chicken tenders can yield dishes both quick and delicious; however, nothing compares with the beautiful presentation of the whole chicken breast over a bed of steaming pasta.

Exercise G_(31)

Answers may vary. This is one possible answer.

Charleston, South Carolina, is a beautiful city filled with tree-lined streets of cobblestone. Visitors can explore the antique and boutique shops; in addition, they can appreciate the city's rich sense of history. There are walking tours of century-old homes and gardens; also, walking enthusiasts can view authentic antebellum plantations. After a day of touring, visitors can recharge at some of Charleston's fine eateries; indeed, the restaurants are among some of the South's most renown. The rich history and picturesque beauty of Charleston is a prominent tourist attraction; however, there are always those tourists who prefer the nearby beaches.

Exercise H_(31)

Answers may vary. This is one possible answer.

San Francisco has enough restaurants and pubs to satisfy more visitors with different palates than any other city its size. Frequent visitors and residents rave about dining in some of the oldest and best seafood eateries on the west coast, but the Tadich Grill, founded during the California Gold Rush days of 1849, is the oldest restaurant in continuous operation in the state.

The waiters wear crisp white jackets, elegantly starched, and they saunter among their well-attended tables with the same dignified manner the place is known for. More steaming dishes of their famous cioppino (pronounced *cho-pino*) make their way to hungry diners than anything else on the menu, for the Tadich Grill is known for its cioppino, one of San Francisco's most delicious edible delights. The hearty seafood stew, full of scallops, prawns, crab, shrimp, halibut, sea bass, and clams, can warm the soul like nothing I have since tasted. No walk can seem colder than down the long city blocks of the city's financial district, when a winter wind blows cold, but when a diner ducks inside the double doors of the Buich building on 240 California Street, an instant warmth rises within.

Mastery Test_(32)

1. B
2. A
3. A
4. C
5. A
6. A
7. A
8. B
9. A
10. C

COMBINING SENTENCES USING SUBORDINATION_(33)

Diagnostic Test_(33)

1. B
2. A
3. B
4. C
5. A
6. The concert hall, which has now grown silent, is filled to capacity.
7. That violinist, who is the youngest orchestra member, is the concertmaster.
8. The older members, who await his entrance, have great respect for him.
9. The young concertmaster, whose mastery is matched by his graciousness, is a favorite among Philadelphia audiences.
10. The young man's proud mother, who lives in Chicago, has come to Philadelphia to see her son.

Exercise A_(34)

1.   B
2.   B
3.   A
4.   B
5.   A
6.   B
7.   A
8.   B
9.   B
10.   A
11.   A
12.   B
13.   A
14.   B
15.   A

Exercise B_(35)

1.   A
2.   **B**
3.   A
4.   **B**
5.   **B**
6.   A
7.   **B**
8.   A
9.   **B**
10.   A
11.   B
12.   A
13.   B
14.   B
15.   A

Exercise C_(37)

1.   A
2.   B
3.   A
4.   C
5.   A
6.   B
7.   C
8.   A
9.   B
10.   B

Exercise D_(38)

1.   A
2.   C
3.   A
4.   B
5.   A
6.   B
7.   C
8.   A
9.   A
10.   B

Exercise E_(40)

Answers may vary. This is one possible revision.

Ann arises in the cold dark and goes to the window, even though the early hour would otherwise take a firm hold of her sleep. A great warm feeling rises from within her, although a thick blanket of newly fallen snow can be seen through the frosted panes. Everywhere, the rural landscape takes on a clean beauty, while sounds are muffled across the fields. Everything is so still, until the wind whips up and wrestles the chimes on the front porch. They send out their lonely sound, breaking the silence of dawn.

Exercise F_(40)

Answers may vary. This is one possible revision.

As John was sleeping, warm beneath the wool army blanket, the radio alarm cut in with the morning weather and travel advisory. Since the storm had arrived as predicted, John jumped up from his warm wraps to brave the cold of his room. Like so many road workers, he seems to enjoy the adversity that snow creates, even if the warm covers on his bed can sometimes seem a whole lot more inviting than the cold dawn. John's sense of duty wins out. Whenever snow covers the city streets, with a promise to paralyze the morning rush, John and the rest of the snow removal crews arrive with giant plows. After the roadways are widened, the plows pushing through to send discarded snow along the curbside, intersections are sanded or covered with rock salt. Few commuters in northern U.S. cities even pause to consider mornings after snowstorms to be any different, because snow removal crews are long gone before the city hall clock chimes 8:00 AM.

Exercise G_(41)

Answers may vary. This is one possible revision.

I have been witness to nothing so methodic as my father's nightly shaving ritual, even though his pre-shaving prelude can have its ever-so-slight variations. The doorway is open just wide enough, so my cat can slither out when the scene gets old for her interest. Because he raises the window to clear the mirror of steam, I struggle to keep my teeth from chattering in the cold dark of the hall, lest he discover my spying. I watch as he removes his wooden handled shaving brush from the metal medicine cabinet, while he fans every bristle to check for some kind of perfection he thinks a shaving brush ought to have. Then, the lather is never hastily applied, until he first runs through a complex series of facial distortions and exercises of some kind. The lather is at last retrieved from the frosted glass shelf above the sink, provided that the skin on his face is adequately stretched and prepared. Finally the lathering begins, as though the prelude has faded, and the symphony of the shave can commence.

Exercise H_(41)

Answers may vary. This is one possible revision.

My father-in-law, for whom I have always felt the warmest regard, usually arrives for his holiday visit with us about a week before. Each day he is with us, which are always among my happiest, we do all kinds of fun pre-holiday things together, like make sugar cookie snowmen with all the detailed trimmings, ride into the city to see all the Christmas displays in department store windows on Fifth Avenue, and wrap and tie all our presents to sounds of *A Bing Crosby Christmas*. Each night my father-in-law and my son, who adores his grandfather, hang more and more ornaments on our little tree.

After I read our night time stories, we tuck Sam into his bed, which oftentimes takes great efforts on my part, and then we go down to enjoy eggnog by the tree. Later, my husband and his father remain downstairs until long after I turn in for the night. Their hushed voices sooth me to sleep.

Exercise I_(42)

Answers may vary. This is one possible answer.

Swimming is one of the best forms of exercise that you can do to exercise without any of the stress of a high-impact activity. It is an excellent aerobic activity, which makes the heart pump more efficiently and helps the lungs take in more air. Swimming also has the benefit of being very low impact, which makes it easier on bones and joints than exercise forms such as running or jumping rope. The low impact of swimming makes it one of the best activities for elderly exercisers, who can be seen enjoying rhythmic laps in health club and outdoor pools across the country.

Exercise J_(42)

Answers may vary. This is one possible answer.

Mention the word "cookie" and almost anyone thinks back to childhood. Practically every American household, that has children, also has a cookie jar. (Of course, adults can also be found to be among some of the most passionate of cookie enthusiasts.) Nevertheless, whatever the variety inside the jar, it's certain there are more clanks made by cookie jar lids than by the lid of any other kitchen container. Cookie aisles, which are the most popular in every grocery store, are probably the most congested at any given time. There is no food more comforting than the cookie, which can be eaten without any preparation like the cooking required of comfort foods such as chicken soup or macaroni and cheese. At the end of a long school day, all a kid needs is strength enough to lift the cookie jar lid and perhaps a loving parent, who can pour the chocolate milk to wash the last crumbs down.

Harcourt, Inc.

Mastery Test_(43)

1. B
2. A
3. B
4. C
5. B
6. C
7. C
8. B
9. B
10. C

CORRECTING THE RUN-ON_(44)

Diagnostic Test_(44)

1. B
2. A
3. A
4. C
5. **B**
6. A
7. A
8. A
9. **B**
10. **B**

Exercise A_(45)

1. C
2. B
3. A
4. A
5. B
6. A
7. C
8. B
9. C
10. B
11. A
12. C
13. C
14. C
15. B

Exercise B_(47)

1. A
2. C
3. A
4. C
5. A

6.	B
7.	A
8.	C
9.	B
10.	A
11.	B
12.	A
13.	A
14.	C
15.	B

Exercise C_(49)

1.	B
2.	B
3.	B
4.	A
5.	B
6.	C
7.	C
8.	C
9.	B
10.	A
11.	B
12.	C
13.	B
14.	B
15.	C

Exercise D_(51)

1.	B
2.	A
3.	C
4.	A
5.	B
6.	C
7.	C
8.	A
9.	B
10.	B
11.	B
12.	C
13.	B
14.	A
15.	B

Harcourt, Inc.

Exercise E_(53)

Answers may vary. This is one possible answer.

Edgar Allan Poe was born in Boston in 1809, and, in spite of many of his harsh critics, his canon of tales and poetry endures strong for many American readers. To those readers, Poe is the great father of the genre of detective fiction. To them, Poe is a great master of mystery and myth, his work brilliantly sprinkled with sly references and allusions. Conversely, the critics have condemned the meaning in Poe's writing as unintelligible, arguing that if readers accept the role of detective while reading his tales, they only arrive at the author's flaw. Readers can search for submerged meaning, only to find that many of the tales tell the same story.

Nevertheless, Poe's own life was somewhat of an American myth. And, what is commonly known about him is of his marriage to Virginia Clemm, his 13-year-old first cousin; however, his poetry and tales will continue to be widely read and enjoyed.

Exercise F_(53)

Answers may vary. This is one possible answer.

Born on July 21, 1899, in Oak Park, Illinois, Ernest Hemingway's life ranged from serving the Italians in WWI as an ambulance driver to being a war correspondent for the Loyalists in Spain. He was a big-game hunter and a bullfighter, and finally he was a winner of the Nobel Prize.

Readers recognize bits of his own life in the characters and themes in his novels and short stories. In his heroes are the ideals by which the author himself lived. His heroes bear the wounds of life's battles; they survive by perservering according to a disaplined code of honor. This code of honor means that human dignity can be achieved in spite of physical perish. Meaning can be experienced in the everyday of human existence.

Exercise G_(54)

Answers may vary. This is one possible answer.

The writings of Zora Neale Hurston are studied most often in connection with the American literary period known as the Harlem Renaissance. From this period came some of the first recognized artistic, musical, and literary expressions of black artists, musicians, and writers.

In Hurston's well-read novel *Their Eyes Were Watching God*, she is recognized for her creation, in its main character Janie, of a notable contrast to the standard stereotypical images of black women in literature. Readers in 1937, the year of the novel's publication, observed in Janie echoes of the author's own searching spirit, her insistence on self-discovery and self-fulfillment on her own terms. More recent readers can see how Hurston seems to foreshadow in her characterization of Janie the stance of many of the modern American women who would come to read the novel throughout the rest of the twentieth century and perhaps beyond.

Exercise H_(55)

Answers may vary. This is one possible revision.

Dear Personnel Director,

This letter responds to your newspaper ad for a Sales Manager to handle the daily workings of the Pleasantville branch of Tricky's Used Stuff Ranch, the best pre-owned stuff sales organization on the East Coast. The talents I acquired while managing the Beanville branch of Sal's Junk Shop will be a perfect fit for the tough hard-charging culture, high-hassle sales training program, and your reputable Stick-To-The-Customer-Like-Glue Bonus Incentive Plan that Tricky's Used Stuff Ranch has become famous for. At Sal's, I learned the value of interrogating employees with a single strong light bulb hanging from the basement ceiling, while spying on employees through 35 cameras and disciplining employees on the sales floor to get superior performance results. I have included several videotapes of my performances, that you will truly enjoy. I hope we can meet as soon as possible to discuss my future with your company. I know I can be an asset to such a quality pre-owned stuff dealer as the Tricky's Used Stuff Ranch franchise, where my exhaustive talents will lead to boatloads of abundant lucrative sales of used stuff to customers who were never more pleased to be separated from their money.

Exercise I_(55)

Answers may vary. This is one possible revision.

To:	**All Sales Associates**
From:	**Slick I. Amm**
Date:	**December 8, 2000**
Re:	**New Sales Manager**

Please give a warm "Tricky Style" welcome to our new Sales Manager Jack Black, who comes from Sal's Junk Shop, the largest junk shop in Beanville. Watch out comrades, for he really knows how shake up the sales floor. Customers left Sal's with armloads of junk and slim wallets due to Jack's unique approach to training sales associates with a military-like discipline. Sal's really moved junk. Jack will be instituting some of his famous techniques here at Tricky's Used Stuff Ranch as soon as he gets his equipment set up in his office in the basement. I can't wait to see the sales climb to the top of the charts! Please distribute the enclosed videotapes to our part-time holiday sales employees, and give them an early taste of Jack's successful sales management approach. I am sure they will be thrilled to be associated with an industry veteran, like Jack who has made such a profound impression on his subordinates.

Mastery Test_(56)

1. B
2. A
3. B
4. A
5. B
6. A
7. A

8.   B
9.   A
10.   B

MAKING SENTENCE PARTS WORK TOGETHER_(58)

Diagnostic Test_(58)

1.   B
2.   C
3.   A
4.   A
5.   B
6.   A
7.   C
8.   B
9.   A
10.   C

PART I: PRONOUNS_(59)

Exercise A_(59)

1.   A
2.   A
3.   **B**
4.   **A**
5.   A
6.   **A**
7.   B
8.   A
9.   B
10.   A
11.   B
12.   A
13.   B
14.   B
15.   A

Exercise B_(60)

1.   A
2.   A
3.   A
4.   B
5.   B
6.   A
7.   B
8.   A
9.   B
10.   A
11.   A

12.   B
13.   B
14.   A
15.   B

Exercise C_(62)

1.   A
2.   B
3.   A
4.   A
5.   A
6.   A
7.   B
8.   A
9.   B
10.   A
11.   A
12.   A
13.   B
14.   A
15.   B

Exercise D_(63)

1.   **Making fresh garden <u>sauce</u> involves using home grown vegetables and herbs as its ingredients.**

2.   **The <u>vegetables and herbs</u> are first gathered from the garden, and they are rinsed well in the kitchen.**

3.   A deep stainless steel sauce <u>pot</u> is best; it should be deep enough for stirring the sauce.

4.   Extra virgin olive <u>oil</u> (about 4 tablespoons) is poured into the pot; let it spread evenly.

5.   Chop about six or seven large <u>cloves</u> of garlic, and add them to the olive oil.

6.   Apply medium heat to the pot; lightly simmer the chopped <u>garlic</u> until its color is light golden.

7.   Coarsely chop the <u>onions, green peppers, and tomatoes</u> and add them to the pot.

8.   Simmer the <u>vegetables</u>, stirring them gently with a wooden spoon.

9.   Mince the fresh <u>herbs</u> (basil, parsley, thyme) and add them to the pot with salt and pepper.

10.   Simmer the <u>sauce</u> for forty minutes without a lid to concentrate its flavors.

11.   The cook should taste the <u>sauce</u> at this point to judge its level of seasoning.

12.   The <u>cook</u> can then adjust the seasoning to suit his or her taste.

13.   The main <u>steps</u> are complete, but these can be varied to the cook's preferences.

14. Tomatoes, green peppers, and onions are the main <u>vegetables</u> in a fresh sauce; however, others, which may be purchased, could be added or substituted.
15. For instance, an imaginative cook could also use <u>mushrooms</u>; they add yet another variation to an old favorite.

Exercise E_(64)

1. C
2. A
3. B
4. B
5. C
6. C
7. B
8. A
9. C
10. A
11. C
12. B
13. A
14. A
15. C

PART II: PARALLEL STRUCTURE AND MODIFIERS_(65)

Exercise F_(65)

1. Some people go into cities, do only what they came to do, and leave as quickly as possible.
2. Others view cities as exciting, entertaining, and interesting.
3. When in San Antonio, I love to eat Tex-mex food, visit the Alamo, and stroll along the River Walk.
4. Some people in New York are fast-paced business executives; others are sightseeing tourists.
5. In New York, the never-sleeping city, you can eat at late-night delis or dance at late-night clubs.
6. New York by day offers rich cultural events and diverse shopping experiences.
7. When I go to Baltimore, I go to the Inner Harbor to shop, to eat, and to enjoy the Aquarium.
8. In St. Louis, the Gateway Arch was begun in 1961, finished in 1965, and dedicated in 1966.
9. Portland, Oregon's more than 200 parks are perfect for leisure, recreation, and sightseeing.
10. While in Portland, some visitors prefer relaxing in Forest Park to shopping and sipping coffee in Powell's City of Books.
11. Seattle offers a mild climate, excellent for shopping, touring, and attending sporting events year round.
12. In Philadelphia, it is fun seeing the Liberty Bell, touring the Betsy Ross House, and strolling in Independence Square.
13. Some Philadelphia tourists would rather catch a quick bite from a street vendor than eat at an upscale Walnut Street restaurant.
14. Various tourist guides are available in most cities; visitors can choose sites, map routes, and note street names.
15. A detailed travel log allows visitors to take notes, write descriptions, and record memories.

Exercise G_(66)

1.	Jake believes that there is a time to shop and a time to garden.
2.	In their marriage, compromise is common and essential for success.
3.	Jake and Lynne are different in their religious beliefs, work ethics, and their disciplining methods for their twins.
4.	However, their home is tranquil, loving, and supportive.
5.	Weekends are a time of shopping, tending the garden, and cooking dinners together.
6.	Lynne's favorite things are playing piano, reading poetry, and riding her bicycle.
7.	Jake prefers playing catch with the boys to spending time indoors on weekends.
8.	The boys admire their parents, who are honest, supportive, and consistent.
9.	The boys study a lot: after school, while dinner is cooking, and in their rooms before bed.
10.	On the weekends they like playing football more than reading or watching TV.
11.	Weekend afternoons are times of ordering pizza, working on model airplanes, and listening to their favorite radio station.
12.	Expressions on their faces reflect their personalities: casual, diligent, content, and intense.
13.	At bedtime, the boys pick out clothes for the next day and hang them on the closet door.
14.	Independent thinking, clear decision making, and respecting others are the boys' traits.
15.	Jake and Lynne are proud of their sons and respectful of their values, too.

Exercise H_(67)

Answers may vary. These are possible answers.

1.	**Clouds appeared to him as majestic mounds of snow, as he looked from the plane window.**
2.	**When he was a young boy, his mother told him many stories of her travels.**
3.	**Then, as his plane was flying low, he could see a herd of cattle.**
4.	**Within a week, students dropped the course on Modernism that Professor Ming taught.**
5.	**Returning their textbooks, the students went to the bookstore, just a short walk across campus.**
6.	**The store clerks accepted all the textbooks from the students who then received their refunds.**
7.	**Only the bookstore manager could issue cash refunds.**
8.	**The store clerks, who were working during the afternoon, could issue the charge credits.**
9.	**The soprano, singing with all clarity, captivated her audience.**
10.	Taking their programs in their hands, the audience left when the concert was over at 10:30.
11.	While in their showers, many opera lovers fantasize about singing one day themselves.
12.	Hopefully, before singing their arias, they will close the bathroom windows.
13.	Opera goers who read the program notes carefully appreciate operas more.
14.	Because the cake was covered with a thick layer of frosting, she knew it would dazzle her guests.
15.	She is completely delighted to serve a well-made dessert.

Exercise I_(68)

Answers may vary. These are possible answers.

1.	Maria was overcome with anticipation and excitement when she arrived in New York.
2.	Since she had traveled for hours, the sight of so many frantic New Yorkers rushing about JFK airport overwhelmed her.
3.	Maria came from a small village in southern Italy, and had never seen so much commotion in a big city.
4.	She was only 17 and quite frightened, and her luggage was piled like a wall around her.
5.	She spoke to a man in a uniform, but the man didn't speak Italian.
6.	So Maria felt lost until a woman showed her a small sign written in Italian.
7.	Maria looked at the sign, but she couldn't make out the words.
8.	Then, Maria recognized her cousin, Tilda, gazing at her with familiar eyes.
9.	I had difficulty locating the letter that was buried under a mountain of books.

10.   I finally found it after I removed the books from the top of my partner's desk.
11.   Since I have always been very organized, the letter would never have left my sight.
12.   As he was driving to California, Jackson saw the Grand Canyon.
13.   Since he was born and raised in the East, the West was a different experience for him.
14.   He daydreamed of the cold winters back in Boston while he was sunning on the warm sand.
15.   With long distance rates being only ten cents a minute on Sunday, he called his parents every week.

Exercise J_(69)

Answers may vary. These are possible answers.

The decision to become full-time, stay-at-home mothers and housewives used to be made for them. Pregnant women who worked always quit their jobs just before having their babies. Family situations are different in our society today. As more and more families are requiring two incomes, this traditional family arrangement is not always the case. Some women are keeping their jobs after delivery, some are scaling back to part-time, and some are participating in job sharing. While many women view themselves as the primary parents responsible for care of their babies, there are some men, whose wives may have the larger salaries, who decide to stay home. With both their parents so carefully considering what is best for them, babies in non-traditional home environments are very fortunate in experiencing the different styles of care often administered by fathers. Whatever the arrangement, it is becoming evident in our society that parenting roles are no longer gender specific.

Exercise K_(70)

Answers may vary. These are possible answers.

New parents who decide to use daycare for their children must also decide on the specific daycare setting. Some children benefit from a surrounding that is socially stimulating, which means it contains other children and maybe a number of caregivers. Some parents of shy children say they can help their children more by exposing them to other children. On the other hand, parents sometimes believe their individual child would benefit more from a more intimate one-on-one care situation, in which the caregiver cares for only the one child. Whether the child attends a daycare center or stays home with his or her home caregiver, the quality of care is the issue. Any caregiver, whether working in a center or in a home, should be warm, compassionate, and encouraging.

Exercise L_(70)

Answers may vary. These are possible answers.

When a new parent, who must work, lives near his or her parents, another childcare option becomes available. Children cared for by enthusiastic grandparents can have the advantage of feeling a genuine love that can significantly strengthen the bond between caregiver and child. Of course, this arrangement doesn't work optimally in all situations. Indeed, certain characteristics must be present for the situation to work for all people involved. This is, basically, that parent should respect grandparent and grandparent should respect parent. The most significant benefit that can come from such a childcare situation is an unconditional love for the child, which sometimes can only come from family members. This is not to mention the added benefit of the monetary savings to the parents, as childcare can be a major expense.

Exercise M_(71)

Answers may vary. These are possible answers.

The idea of staying home to care for <u>their</u> children while at the same time <u>returning to work to resume</u> the responsibilities of their jobs has suggested another childcare option for working parents. Telecommuting -- working from home with a connection to the office -- has grown increasingly popular among parents with young children. The "fantasy" of telecommuting is that it can allow working parents to be in two places at the same time. This fantasy has become a reality with the connection capabilities of <u>modems, e-mail, fax machines, and the Internet</u>. Many supervisors of workers with proven performance are so happy for the ability to keep such valued employees that <u>they are</u> becoming more receptive to the idea of telecommuting.

Mastery Test_(71)

1. B
2. A
3. A
4. A
5. A
6. B
7. C
8. B
9. C
10. B

PRACTICING MORE WITH VERBS_(72)

Diagnostic Test_(72)

1. B
2. A
3. C
4. A
5. B
6. B
7. C
8. A
9. A
10. A

Exercise A_(73)

1. A
2. A
3. C
4. B
5. A
6. C
7. B
8. A
9. C

10.   B
11.   A
12.   B
13.   B
14.   B
15.   A

Exercise B_(75)

1.   A
2.   C
3.   C
4.   A
5.   B
6.   B
7.   A
8.   C
9.   B
10.   B
11.   A
12.   C
13.   B
14.   A
15.   A

Exercise C_(77)

1.	P	My father-in-law greatly enjoyed the dish of berries.
2.	A	They were eaten by him with much appreciation.
3.	P	I hand-picked them.
4.	P	I selected only the plumpest, ripest ones.
5.	A	At home they were sliced and sugared.
6.	A	They were turned very gently in the crystal bowl.
7.	A	Cream was also poured over them.
8.	P	Heat scorched the July afternoon.
9.	A	However, our backyard was shaded by the enormous sycamore.
10.	A	We were sheltered from the sun by its cool shade.
11.	P	Later my father-in-law made lemonade from fresh lemons.
12.	P	The cold liquid refreshed us.
13.	P	Soon we saw large storm clouds rolling in.
14.	P	We heard thunder off in the distance.
15.	A	The storm's theatrics were enjoyed from the front porch.

Exercise D_(78)

That gloomy night, an angry wind blew so hard that the branches of the large oak tree tapped continually at his window. Soon, the small child was so frightened by the storm that he crept into his parents' room. As always, his parents had been soundly sleeping and heard nothing. As he sat quietly on the floor, by his mother's side of the bed, he thought he saw a large arm out through his parents' window. At once he started shivering. He then crawled into bed next to his mother, closed his eyes tight to shut it all out, and awoke finally to the morning sun shining brilliantly in the same sky that appeared so ominous the night before.

Exercise E_(78)

It <u>seemed</u> to her that he could <u>have</u> come to her parents' New Year's Eve party dressed much better than he <u>was</u>. Now she <u>knows</u> that her parents and the rest of her relatives <u>will</u> be commenting on her new boyfriend's appearance the next day. If only she <u>weren't</u> always being <u>compared</u> to her sister. Her sister's husband is a doctor and he is always <u>seen</u> in finely tailored suits or freshly starched and ironed sportswear.

Her boyfriend Jimmy could never, or almost never, be <u>caught</u> in a suit. His normal attire consisted mostly of what he referred to as "vintage" jeans and black T-shirts. Vintage for Jimmy meant horizontal slashes <u>cut</u> in the legs of the threadbare jeans. The T-shirt he wore <u>had</u> its own array of holes, tears, and bleached out spots. He looked more like he was dressed for an alternative rock club than for her parents' party where he would be meeting the rest of her very conservative family. She wondered if she should <u>have</u> <u>told</u> him that the party was going to be a bit formal.

Exercise F_(79)

Even before they <u>began</u> to date, Kate <u>had known</u> that Jimmy was a unique individualist. They had <u>met</u> in a film class the spring semester of their sophomore year, and ever since then they <u>have been</u> friends. On their first study date, Jimmy <u>brought</u> her a mason jar filled with every type of flower he <u>had seen</u> growing along the roads he <u>had taken</u> to get to her apartment. She was so charmed by Jimmy's gesture that she <u>thought</u> <u>she would have married</u> him that very day if he <u>had asked</u>.

Months had passed since that first date, and together they enjoyed exhibits at the Art Institute of Chicago, moonlit picnics along the lake, and hikes through snow-filled woods at his father's cabin. At that very moment, in her parents' dining room, she wished she <u>were</u> in those woods again, holding Jimmy's strong hand. The only comforting thought she had was that as her stuffy old Aunt Gertrude, in her red taffeta and pearls, was whispering to Uncle Robert, Jimmy sat next to her <u>enjoying the Beethoven</u> concerto her brother was playing on the piano, and didn't seem to know anything was unusual at all. Then, she <u>knew</u> that he <u>had</u> outclassed them all, making a place for himself wherever he was.

Mastery Test_(79)

1. B
2. C
3. C
4. B
5. A
6. A
7. B
8. C
9. C
10. B

USING CORRECT CAPITALIZATION AND PUNCTUATION_(81)

Diagnostic Test_(81)

1. B
2. A
3. C
4. A
5. A

6.   A
7.   B
8.   B
9.   B
10.   B

Exercise A_(82)

1.   B
2.   B
3.   A
4.   B
5.   B
6.   B
7.   A
8.   B
9.   B
10.   A
11.   B
12.   B
13.   A
14.   **B**
15.   **A**

Exercise B_(83)

1.   **A**
2.   **B**
3.   **B**
4.   **B**
5.   A
6.   B
7.   B
8.   A
9.   A
10.   A
11.   B
12.   A
13.   A
14.   A
15.   A

Exercise C_(84)

1.   A
2.   B
3.   A
4.   B
5.   B
6.   B
7.   A
8.   A
9.   A

10.	B
11.	B
12.	B
13.	A
14.	A
15.	A

Exercise D_(85)

1.	A
2.	B
3.	A
4.	B
5.	A
6.	B
7.	A
8.	B
9.	A
10.	A
11.	A
12.	A
13.	A
14.	**A**
15.	**B**

Exercise E_(86)

1.	**A**
2.	**B**
3.	**B**
4.	C
5.	C
6.	C
7.	C
8.	B
9.	C
10.	B

Exercise F_(88)

1.	B
2.	A
3.	C
4.	B
5.	A
6.	A
7.	C
8.	C
9.	B
10.	A
11.	C
12.	A

13. B
14. A
15. A

Exercise G_(90)

1. A
2. B
3. B
4. A
5. C
6. A
7. A
8. A
9. B
10. C
11. B
12. C
13. A
14. A
15. B

Exercise H_(92)

The Harlem <u>Renaissance</u> has come to be noted for the resurgence of <u>African-American</u> art. Literature, knowledge, and the arts of <u>African-Americans,</u> who had already gained respect for their works in <u>Europe,</u> had finally found an open door at home in the <u>United States</u>. Poets, writers, musicians, intellectuals, and entrepreneurs had found a place for themselves. In the <u>1920s (or 1920's),</u> <u>Harlem, New York,</u> became a fertile cultural center that fostered and stimulated the arts of so many. Musicians such as <u>Duke Ellington, Louis Armstrong, and Eubie Blake,</u> just to name a very few, joined their musical expression with the written expression of writers such as <u>Langston Hughes, Dorothy West, Zora Neale Hurston, and Countee Cullen</u>. Visual arts and theater depicted the <u>political, social, and economic conditions</u> of being black in America. The time period remains one of the most uplifting to African-Americans as artists.

Exercise I_(92)

Equally as significant as the pasta craze of the <u>1980s (or 1980's)</u> is <u>today's</u> rice popularity. <u>Traditionally,</u> the availability of rice in <u>American</u> supermarkets was either plain white rice or converted rice. <u>Today's</u> consumers can choose from many more varieties. Rice enthusiasts can purchase from <u>a growing range of rices: Thai Jasmine rice , California Wehani, Japanese rice, Louisiana pecan, black rice, red rice, and short- and long-grain sticky rice.</u>

There are countless strains of rice varieties world-wide. Most of these originated in <u>East Asia,</u> where most of the <u>world's</u> rice is still raised. <u>However,</u> rice can be grown on almost any <u>continent</u> in radically diverse environments. <u>For example,</u> rice can grow in flooded tropical paddies or in irrigated deserts. It is the diversity of these growing conditions, as well as the difference in the seeds <u>themselves,</u> that account for the distinct <u>color, flavor, and aroma</u> of rices.

Exercise J_(93)

J.D. Salinger was born Jerome David Salinger in <u>New York City</u> on January 1, 1919. He attended Valley Forge Military <u>A</u>cademy, in Pennsylvania, and he graduated in 1936. After his draft into the United States <u>A</u>rmy in 1942, and discharge in 1945, he began publishing his short stories regularly in some of the bigger magazines, like the *Saturday Evening Post, Esquire,* and the *New Yorker.* His publishing career became most defined by a long relationship with the *New Yorker,* beginning in the late 1940s. Then, in 1951, his novel *The Catcher in the Rye* was published and becomes the work that Salinger is most well known for today.

Exercise K_(93)

Laura, my friend <u>Robert's</u> maternal <u>grandmother</u>, was known to him as a simple woman who took care of her husband and six children, while at the same time she cared for three children from her neighborhood. She always seemed to honor nothing more than the <u>Ten Commandments,</u> her <u>husband</u>, and her children. <u>"These things," she often said to him, "are the things that matter."</u> She took great pride in her home and in her property, and she held cleanliness and organization in high regard. She made all of her <u>children's</u> clothing, and to this day I have never seen such careful detail, such precision. Robert inherited his <u>grandmother's</u> cedar chest after she died last <u>fall,</u> and along with countless old photos, <u>birthday cards</u>, and past issues of *<u>Ladies Home Journal</u>,* some of his <u>mother's</u> school dresses are still inside, wrapped neatly in tissue.

Mastery Test_(94)

1. B
2. A
3. A
4. A
5. C
6. C
7. C
8. A
9. A
10. B

PAYING ATTENTION TO LOOK-ALIKES AND SOUND-ALIKES_(95)

Diagnostic Test_(95)

1. A
2. A
3. A
4. A
5. B
6. B
7. A
8. A
9. B
10. B

Harcourt, Inc.

Exercise A_(95)

1.	B
2.	B
3.	C
4.	C
5.	A
6.	B
7.	B
8.	A
9.	B
10.	C
11.	A
12.	A
13.	C
14.	B
15.	A

Exercise B_(97)

1.	B
2.	A
3.	C
4.	A
5.	A
6.	B
7.	B
8.	A
9.	C
10.	A
11.	B
12.	A
13.	A
14.	C
15.	B

Exercise C_(99)

1.	C
2.	A
3.	B
4.	C
5.	B
6.	C
7.	C
8.	C
9.	A
10.	A
11.	A
12.	B
13.	C
14.	B
15.	B

Exercise D_(100)

When I was a small child, every Sunday in July and August my grandparents would take my sister and me to Atlantic City. In those days there were no casinos, just grand Moorish hotels that lined the Boardwalk. The Boardwalk was always filled with strolling tourists whose only clothes were bathing suits. Benches lined the railings where those who rested gazed out across the beach to the sea. Of course, there were the grand amusement piers that stretched out from the Boardwalk. At night, when the tide was high, the water would come up right under the Boardwalk. You could look out over the rail and see the sea below, with moonlight reflecting off the waves.

Exercise E_(107)

Probably the most famous of these grand amusement piers was the Steel Pier. As well as carousels and other amusements, there were various shows and animal acts on the pier. At night, the place was quite a spectacle. There were many exciting things to see there. However, the one thing that stands out vividly in my memory is the famous Diving Horse show. A beautiful girl would ride a horse up a ramp to a platform high above a large pool of water. After they were at the top, to the crowd's amazement, horse and diver would dive right off the platform and plunge into the water below. Then the whole crowd would applaud wildly with the big splash.

Exercise F_(107)

In the midst of all that cheering, however, I always felt quite sad. I wondered if given a choice, the horse would choose to do something that seemed to me so unnatural for a horse to do. But alas, going to the Diving Horse Show was a summer custom to most people who vacationed at the New Jersey seashore. I just couldn't stop thinking about that horse when the show was over. I'd do the same thing each timeùwalk back out on the Boardwalk past the salt-water taffy stand, clutch my grandfather's hand, breathe in the salt air, and shiver at the thought of it all. It's a memory I'll always carry with me.

Mastery Test_(102)

1.   B
2.   A
3.   B
4.   A
5.   A
6.   B
7.   A
8.   A
9.   A
10. A

IRREGULAR VERBS_(103)

Diagnostic Test_(103)

1.   B
2.   C
3.   A
4.   C

5.	A
6.	B
7.	A
8.	A
9.	C
10.	A

Exercise A_(104)

1.	A
2.	C
3.	A
4.	A
5.	C
6.	A
7.	B
8.	A
9.	A
10.	C
11.	C
12.	C
13.	A
14.	C
15.	B

Exercise B_(105)

1.	A
2.	A
3.	A
4.	B
5.	A
6.	B
7.	A
8.	A
9.	C
10.	C
11.	B
12.	A
13.	A
14.	A
15.	A

Exercise C_(106)

1.	B
2.	A
3.	C
4.	B
5.	A
6.	B
7.	B
8.	B

9. C
10. C
11. A
12. C
13. C
14. B
15. C

Exercise D_(108)

1. B
2. B
3. A
4. B
5. A
6. A
7. B
8. C
9. A
10. A
11. B
12. A
13. B
14. A
15. A

Exercise E_(110)

There in the middle of the forest <u>stood</u> a rustic cabin. As we walked through the door, all at once the smell of cedar <u>brought</u> back so many memories of my childhood summers at the lake. One would almost think with all the years that I would have <u>forgotten</u> how much I loved those timesùthe hikes through the woods, the fire crackling as we ate fresh trout we <u>had caught</u> that afternoon. But I recall nights watching the fireflies dot the darkness across the lake, believing I had never <u>seen</u> a sight so peaceful. Now I look up through the cabin window to the clarity of the stars in the blackest sky I have ever <u>seen</u>, and I know with all certainty I have not <u>lost</u> sight of things past nor <u>forgotten</u> their beauty.

Exercise F_(110)

Dear Carmella,

When the guests arrive, I do not believe they will have <u>eaten</u>. I spoke to them at noon when they stopped for lunch. They said they were driving non-stop the rest of the way. After their long drive, they will probably have <u>grown</u> quite hungry and tired. They will have <u>ridden</u> all day without stopping for dinner. It would be nice to leave a tray of assorted grapes, cheeses, crackers, and meats in their room. Leave a chilled bottle of Chardonnay. After they have <u>gotten</u> a chance to relax a bit, go in with the basket of menus from the restaurants in town. Let them go to dinner. While they're gone, it would be nice to go in and turn down the sheets and leave a tray of chocolates and some of our vintage port. Tomorrow, after they have <u>slept</u>, they will be ready for our tour. The road along the coast should offer them sights they have never <u>seen</u>. I will be back late in the afternoon and will greet them then. Thanks so much for covering for me

Mastery Test_(111)

1. B
2. A
3. A
4. B
5. B
6. B
7. A
8. A
9. C
10. A